Contents

Introduction to *Asbestos essentials*: Advice to managers and sole traders on *Asbestos essentials* 1

Why is asbestos a problem? 1
Who this manual is for and how to use it 2
What you need to do 3
Does the work need a licence? 4
Decision flow chart 7
Disposal of asbestos materials and waste 9

Equipment and Method sheets

EM1 What to do if you uncover or damage materials that may contain asbestos 11

EM2 Training 14

EM3 Building and dismantling a mini-enclosure 15

EM4 Using a Class H vacuum cleaner for asbestos 17

EM5 Wetting asbestos materials 21

EM6 Personal protective equipment (PPE) 23

EM7 Using damp rags to clean surfaces of minor asbestos contamination 27

EM8 Personal decontamination 29

EM9 Disposal of asbestos waste 31

EM10 Statement of cleanliness after textured coating removal 33

Task sheets

A1 Drilling holes in asbestos insulating board (AIB) 35

A2 Removing a single (screwed-in) asbestos insulating board (AIB) ceiling tile 39

A3 Removing a door with asbestos insulating board (AIB) fireproofing 43

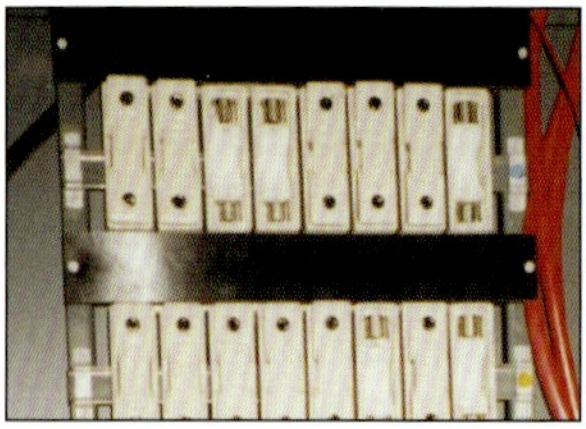

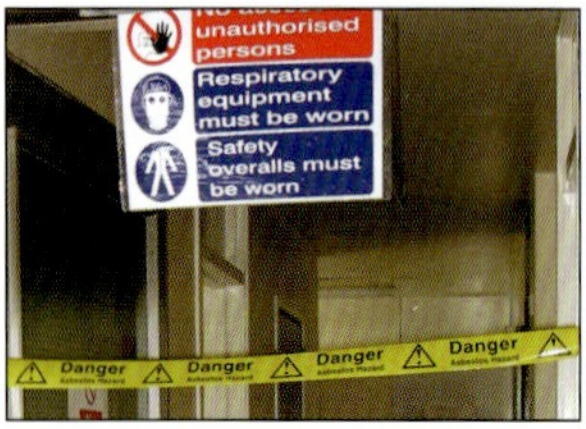

A4 Removing a single asbestos insulating board (AIB) panel less than $1m^2$, fixed with nails or screws 45

A5 Cleaning light fittings attached to asbestos insulating board (AIB) 49

A6 Repairing minor damage to asbestos insulating board (AIB) 51

A7 Painting undamaged asbestos insulating board (AIB) 53

A8 Enclosing undamaged asbestos materials to prevent impact damage 55

A9 Drilling holes in asbestos cement (AC) and other highly bonded materials 57

A10 Cleaning debris from guttering on an asbestos cement (AC) roof 61

A11 Removing asbestos cement (AC) debris 63

A12 Cleaning weathered asbestos cement (AC) roofing and cladding 65

A13 Repairing damaged asbestos cement (AC) 69

A14 Removing asbestos cement (AC) sheets, gutters, etc and dismantling a small AC structure 71

A15 Removing an asbestos cement (AC) or reinforced plastic product, eg tank, duct, water cistern 75

A16 Painting asbestos cement (AC) sheets 79

A17 Removing asbestos paper linings 81

A18 Removing asbestos friction linings 85

A19 Removing an asbestos fire blanket 87

A20 Laying cables in areas containing undamaged asbestos materials 89

A21 Removing asbestos-containing bituminous products 91

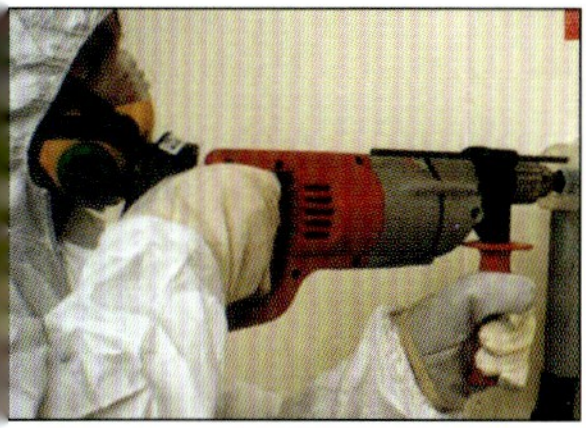

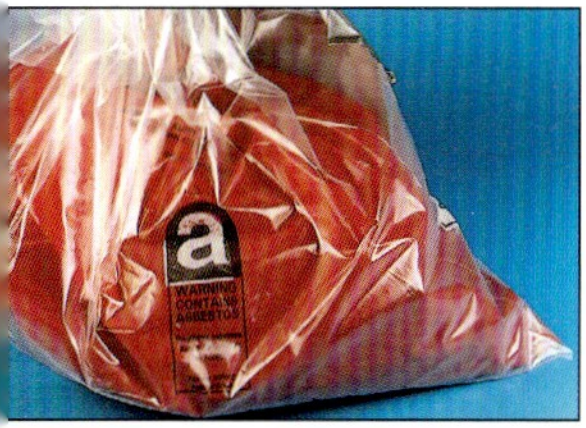

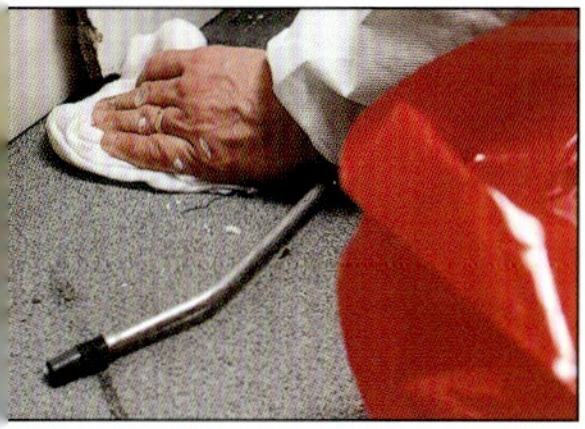

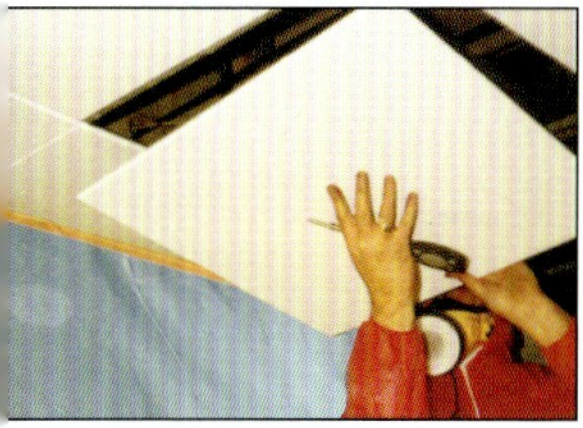

A22 Removing metal cladding lined with asbestos-containing bitumen 94

A23 Removing asbestos-containing floor tiles and mastic 97

A24 Removing flexible asbestos textile duct connectors (gaiters) 101

A25 Removing compressed asbestos fibre (CAF) gaskets and asbestos rope seals 104

A26 Drilling and boring through textured coatings 107

A27 Inserting and removing screws through textured coatings 111

A28 Removing textured coating from a small area, eg 1 square metre 114

A29 Clearing up debris following collapse of a ceiling or wall covered with textured coating 117

A30 Removing an asbestos-containing 'Arc shield' from electrical switchgear 119

A31 Removing a single asbestos-containing gas or electric heater 121

A32 Replacing an asbestos-containing part in a 'period' domestic appliance 124

A33 Replacing an asbestos-containing fusebox or a single fuse assembly 127

A34 Removing pins and nails from an asbestos insulating board (AIB) panel 131

A35 Replacing an asbestos cement (AC) flue or duct 133

A36 Removing an asbestos cement (AC) panel outside, beside or beneath a window 136

A37 Removing asbestos-containing mastic, sealant, beading, filler, putty or fixing 139

A38 How to deal with fly-tipped asbestos waste 141

Introduction to *Asbestos essentials:* Advice to managers and sole traders on *Asbestos essentials*

This book tells employers, managers and sole-traders what to do when they need to work on or near asbestos-containing materials (ACMs). It will help you to decide what category of asbestos work it is and how to plan the work safely.

Most work with asbestos-containing materials, including lagging, insulation and insulating board, must be done by an HSE-licensed contractor.

Asbestos essentials covers work that does not need a licence, if carried out as the sheets describe. Each sheet describes 'good practice' for a particular task and covers the action needed to reduce exposure to an adequate level.

Asbestos-related disease

Disturbing asbestos-containing material can release invisible fibres. Once in the air, fibres can be breathed in and cause lung diseases including:

- mesothelioma – a cancer of the linings to the lungs and stomach;
- lung cancer; and
- asbestosis – lung scarring.

There are no sudden changes in health after breathing in fibres – these diseases can take from 15 to 60 years to develop. They are incurable and often fatal. You need to protect yourself now to prevent contracting an asbestos-related disease in the future.

Why is asbestos a problem?

Large amounts of asbestos were used in new and refurbished buildings before 2000. Usage began to decline in the 1970s and blue asbestos (crocidolite) had a voluntary ban in 1970. Blue and brown (amosite) asbestos were banned by law in 1985. Uses of white asbestos (chrysotile) were banned in 1999. Everything else, and most second-hand supply (except for very high performance materials) was banned by 2000. Therefore, all supply of materials containing asbestos is banned, including making materials available to a third party in any way, whether or not for any payment.

A large number of premises and older plant and equipment still contain some form of asbestos. Much of the asbestos will be hidden in the fabric of the building so

Some trades likely to disturb asbestos

Anyone who works on the fabric of a building may be at risk of disturbing asbestos. This includes:

- electricians, joiners, plumbers, gas fitters, shop fitters, heating and ventilation engineers;
- labourers, roofers, plasterers, demolition workers and other workers in construction;
- phone and data engineers, alarm installers; and
- surveyors, general maintenance engineers, painters and decorators.

not immediately obvious – it is also unlikely to be recorded in the building plans. Workers most likely to come into contact with asbestos-containing products are those in the construction, maintenance, refurbishment and related trades. When asbestos materials are damaged or disturbed they can release dangerous fibres which, if breathed in, can cause serious diseases. Around 4500 people in Great Britain die every year from asbestos-related diseases, making asbestos the single greatest cause of work-related deaths.

Who this manual is for, and how to use it

This manual will help small businesses, sub-contractors and the self-employed comply with the Control of Asbestos Regulations 2012. It will also help dutyholders, clients, trade union and employee safety representatives understand how work should be done.

Asbestos essentials provides the information you need to help you recognise asbestos and protect yourself, containing:

- a series of 38 task sheets with full colour images, illustrations and step-by-step guidance. It is important to follow all the actions in a task sheet, or use equally effective measures. Following the sheets will help reduce the risk of ill health from asbestos;
- equipment and method (em) sheets with extra guidance on getting the right tools for the job and how to use them. Each task sheet has a list of em sheets you should read before you start that task;
- a flow chart to help you decide if you can carry out the work or you need to use an HSE-licensed contractor, or whether you need to notify – see page 7;

- a detailed illustration of an 'asbestos building' showing some of the most common places asbestos is likely to be found – see the inside back cover;
- a safety checklist to help you make sure you haven't forgotten anything – see page 144;
- 'More help' – a list of places to look for further information – see page 143.

What you need to do

- Before starting work you need to check what asbestos is present, in commercial properties there should be a plan/register – ask to see it. You need to check that the plan covers the area of the building that you will be working in and if you are doing refurbishment work that it includes a survey that tells you what types of asbestos is present and it's condition. If there is no register or survey or the report is not clear – do not start work. Alternatively, you can assume that any material you need to disturb does contain asbestos. The client also needs to see your plan of work to understand what work you are going to do, and how.

Licensed work – Don't touch this!

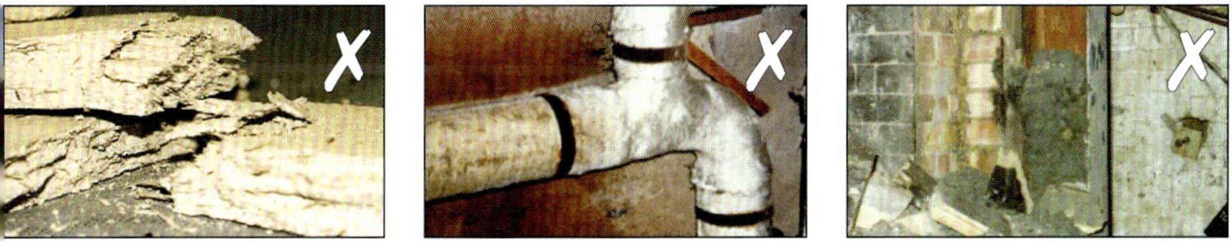

Broken asbestos insulating board, asbestos lagging and sprayed asbestos (limpet)

Non-licensed work – Do this if you are trained

Damaged textured coating, asbestos cement roofing and an asbestos-containing gasket

If you have any doubts, carry out a risk assessment (see 'More help') or ask the client to employ an HSE–licensed asbestos contractor

Your workers

- Everyone who works with, or may disturb asbestos, must be properly trained (including the self-employed). See sheet em2.

What the premises owner (client) needs to tell you

- Where any asbestos containing materials (or materials presumed to contain asbestos) are, that you are likely to meet. The information provided should be specific.

Main points

- You need training to work safely with ACMs. See sheet em2.
- *Asbestos essentials* does not apply to licensed work. You should only go ahead if you are sure the work does not require a licence.
- Work with, or disturbance of, any type of ACM can be dangerous.
- Second-hand equipment may not be asbestos-free.
- If you work on ACMs and you smoke, you are at much greater risk of lung cancer.
- Consider those around you. Don't put your workmates in danger or take fibres home on your clothes and put your family at risk.
- Carry out the work and dispose of contaminated materials safely.

Does the work need a licence?

Most work with asbestos needs to be carried out by a licensed contractor. This includes work on asbestos coating and asbestos lagging; and work on asbestos insulation or asbestos insulating board (AIB) where the risk assessment demonstrates that the fibre release will be high, eg the material is badly damaged, or the work is not short duration work.

'Short duration' means any one person doing this type of work for less than one hour, or more people doing the work for a total of less than two hours, in any seven consecutive days. The total time spent by all workers must not exceed two hours. This includes time spent setting up, cleaning and clearing up.

Non-licensed work includes work on asbestos-containing textured coatings and asbestos cement.

Is it notifiable non-licensed work?

From April 2012, some non-licensed work, where the risk of fibre release is greater, is subject to three additional requirements – notification of work, medical examinations and record keeping (the requirement for medical examinations does not come into force until April 2015). This work is known as notifiable non-licensed work (NNLW).

To decide if the work is NNLW, you will need to consider the type of work you are going to carry out, the type of material you are going to work on and its condition:

- **Decide what type of work you are doing:**
  - **Maintenance** – eg drilling holes to attach fittings or pass cables through, painting, cleaning etc. Maintenance includes some removal where it is incidental to the main task, eg removing an asbestos ceiling tile to allow inspection; or
  - **Removal** – eg as part of a refurbishment or redesign project; or
  - **Encapsulation** – eg work to enclose or seal asbestos materials in good condition; or
  - **Air monitoring and control, and the collection and analysis of samples.**

- **Consider the asbestos type:**
  - Is it **friable?** – the more friable a material is, the more likely it will release asbestos fibres when worked on and the greater the risk of exposure. Materials such as asbestos insulation are more friable than materials such as asbestos cement; and
  - **How firmly is the asbestos bonded in a matrix?** (For removal work only) – Asbestos containing materials (ACMs) where the asbestos is coated,

covered or contained within another material, such as cement, paint or plastic are considered to be firmly bonded in a matrix; and

- **Consider the material's condition:**
  - **Has the material been damaged or is it in poor condition?** – eg badly flood or firedamaged; and
  - **Will the materials' matrix be destroyed when worked on?** – eg deteriorating textured decorative coatings ('Artex') with gel or steam.

Once you've considered these three elements, the decision flow chart opposite will help you to decide which category your work with asbestos is, or check the HSE website for more help before you start.

In summary, most work with firmly bonded materials in good condition such as asbestos cement, bitumen, plastic, resin, rubber, roofing felt, paper linings, cardboard, textiles, gaskets, washers and rope etc will not need to be notified. Short duration 'maintenance' work involving AIB which is in good condition will also not normally need to be notified, NNLW will normally include short duration maintenance and removal work with asbestos insulation, removal of textured decorative coatings where the material is destroyed eg by scraping it off, and short duration removal of AIB as part of refurbishment.

Decision flow chart

Use this simple flow chart to help you decide who needs to do the work.

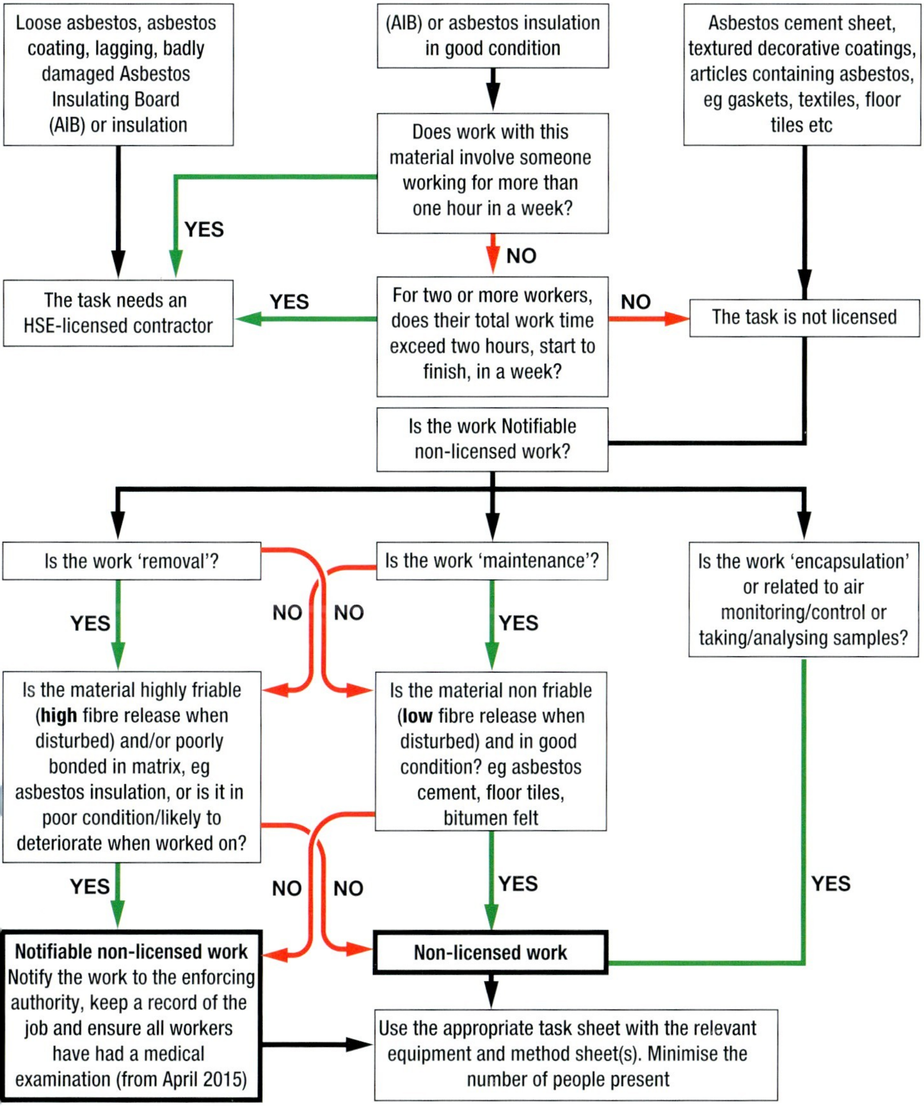

OTHER HAZARDS

Other specific hazards appear in the checklist on each *Asbestos essentials* task sheet. They include:

Work on fragile roofs – see www.hse.gov.uk/construction/index.htm. Fragile roofs cannot bear weight.

Work at height – see www.hse.gov.uk/falls/index.htm. Take precautions to avoid falls. Must you work from a ladder? Where necessary, erect an access platform.

Electrical hazards – see www.hse.gov.uk/electricity/index.htm. Get a competent electrician to isolate and reconnect the electricity supply.

Manual handling – see www.hse.gov.uk/msd/index.htm. Plan how to remove and handle heavy material and articles safely.

Slips and trips – see www.hse.gov.uk/slips/index.htm. Floors protected with polythene become very slippery when wet.

Confined spaces – see www.hse.gov.uk/confinedspace/index.htm. You need to know that restricted workplaces are safe to enter and the air is fit to breathe.

There may be other hazards – you need to consider them all.

Planning

Before carrying out any work:

- Ask the premises owners for their records of asbestos; what was checked, what was found, and what was not checked.
- If there is no record and you have reason to suspect asbestos, ask for an asbestos survey to be done before accepting the contract (you will have to check yourself in domestic properties).
- Check if the work could require a licence – see 'More help'.
- When a licence is not needed for the work, check if the work is NNLW and if so follow the requirements and then follow the task sheets or other HSE guidance.
- If there is no task sheet for the work, get help from a competent health and safety advisor.
- When you seek advice, ensure that the person providing that advice is competent.
- If asbestos-containing material needs replacement, the replacement must be asbestos-free.

Prepare a short plan of work. If the work is NNLW, your copy of the notification may help you. Make sure the plan includes the following:

- what the work is, and how long it is likely to last;
- the address and description of the job;
- when the work will be done;
- the procedures to follow to reduce exposure and prevent the spread of asbestos, ie by following the *Asbestos essentials* task sheets;
- the equipment needed, including personal protective equipment (PPE);
- decontamination and waste disposal arrangements; and
- emergency procedures.

See *equipment and method (em)* sheets for useful advice to help you prepare this plan.

Make sure that everyone involved is fully aware of the plan and knows:

SAFETY CHECKLIST

- ✔ Can you avoid disturbing asbestos by doing the job in some other way?
- ✔ Do you need a licence for the work?
- ✔ Always follow all legal requirements.
- ✔ Follow the task guidance sheet.
- ✔ Use an asbestos waste container.
- ✔ Dispose at a licensed disposal site.

Caution:

- Don't sweep up dust or debris – use a Class H vacuum cleaner or damp rags.
- Don't take used overalls home.
- Don't reuse disposable PPE.
- Don't smoke.
- Don't eat or drink in the work area.

Danger sign

- what they need to do;
- how to wear their PPE and RPE correctly;
- why each action is being taken; and
- what to do in the case of emergencies and accidents.

Manage the work

- Monitor the work to ensure it is being carried out with the appropriate controls.

Caution: Emergency callout is no excuse for low standards or cutting corners.

Disposal of asbestos materials and waste

'Hazardous' or 'Special' waste needs safe disposal. This includes:

- asbestos;
- materials containing asbestos; and
- anything contaminated with asbestos, unless fully decontaminated.

Make sure you double-bag and label asbestos waste.

For advice on disposal contact the Local Authority, the Environment Agency or, if based in Scotland, SEPA. Or hire a licensed waste contractor – see 'More help' and em9.

Asbestos label

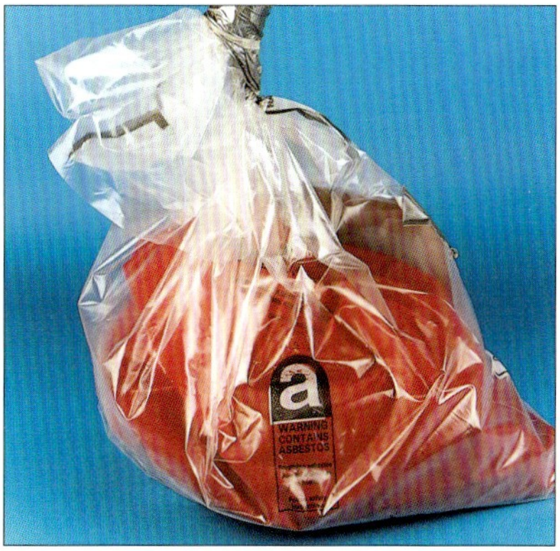

Double-bagged waste

Don't create dust if you can avoid it

Using a Class H vacuum cleaner and a drill cowl

em1 asbestos essentials

Non-licensed tasks

What to do if you uncover or damage materials that may contain asbestos

Equipment and method sheet

Asbestos isn't always obvious. Would you spot an asbestos gasket on an old engine, asbestos cement pipes or an asbestos-containing fuse board? If you're not sure, the premises owner needs to get it checked out!

There are three 'colours' of asbestos, but you can't tell just by the colour what you have found; it could be mixed with other ingredients which change its appearance.

Remember:

- Asbestos fibres can cause lung cancer and lung diseases.
- Check what you're working on before you start.
- Read the safety checklist.

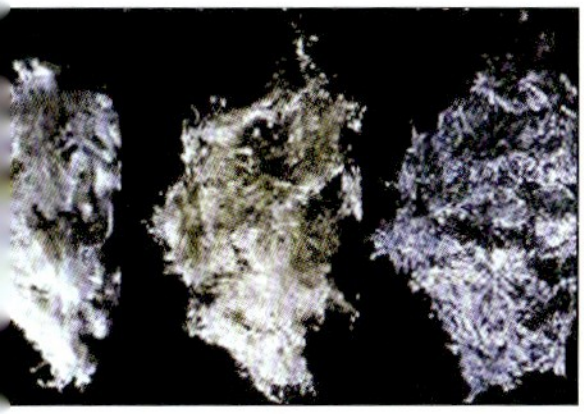

What this sheet covers

This sheet shows some examples of where you can find asbestos. A chart describes what to do if you find asbestos materials during a job.

It also applies where asbestos materials get damaged by accident.

Procedures

- Stop this work immediately.
- Follow the chart on the opposite page or do a risk assessment to decide who must do the work – you may need a licensed contractor.
- Minimise the spread of contamination to other areas.
- Keep exposures as low as you can.
- Clean up the contamination.

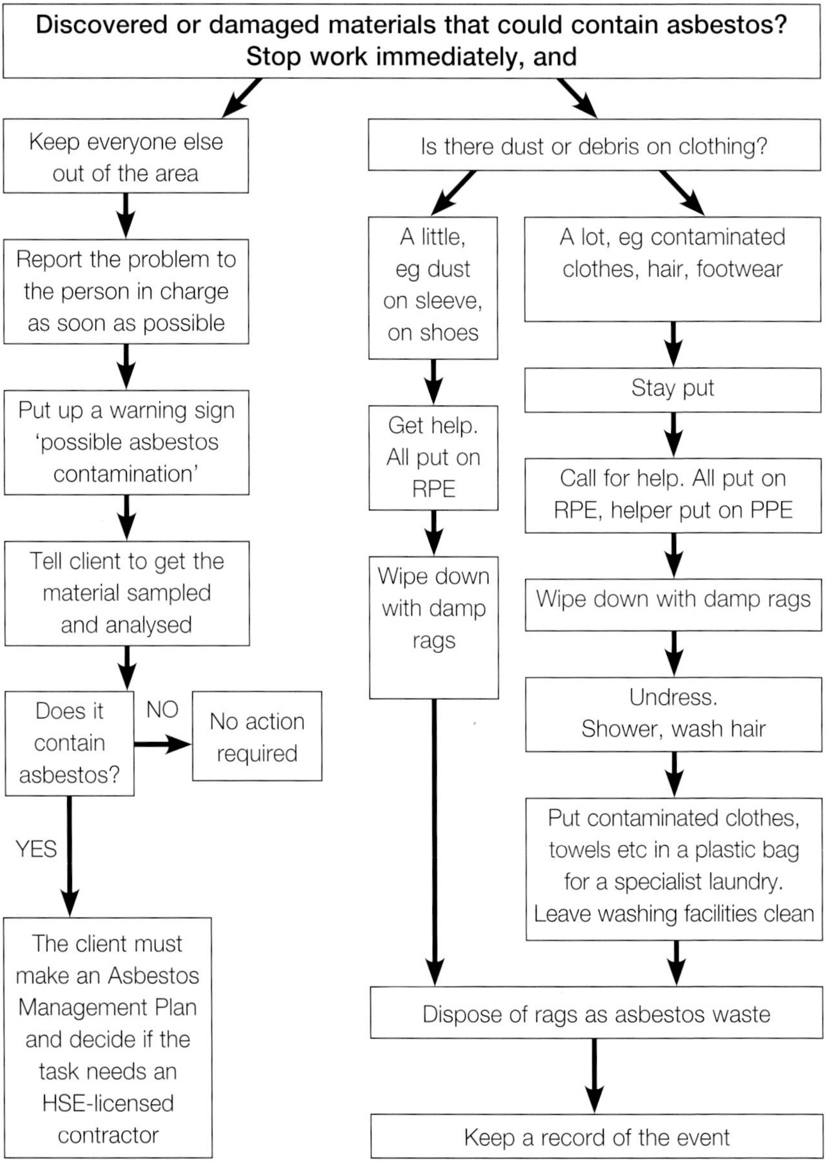
Discovered or damaged materials that could contain asbestos? Stop work immediately, and
Keep everyone else out of the area
Report the problem to the person in charge as soon as possible
Put up a warning sign 'possible asbestos contamination'
Tell client to get the material sampled and analysed
Does it contain asbestos?
NO
No action required
YES
The client must make an Asbestos Management Plan and decide if the task needs an HSE-licensed contractor
Is there dust or debris on clothing?
A little, eg dust on sleeve, on shoes
Get help. All put on RPE
Wipe down with damp rags
A lot, eg contaminated clothes, hair, footwear
Stay put
Call for help. All put on RPE, helper put on PPE
Wipe down with damp rags
Undress. Shower, wash hair
Put contaminated clothes, towels etc in a plastic bag for a specialist laundry. Leave washing facilities clean
Dispose of rags as asbestos waste
Keep a record of the event

Top row: An asbestos gasket, asbestos cement pipes and an asbestos-containing fuse board
Bottom row: The asbestos cement pipes are labelled, so are the tiles, but you might not know until you start to lift them. There could be sprayed limpet under the asbestos cement (AC) sheeting

Asbestos insulating board (AIB) fire surround

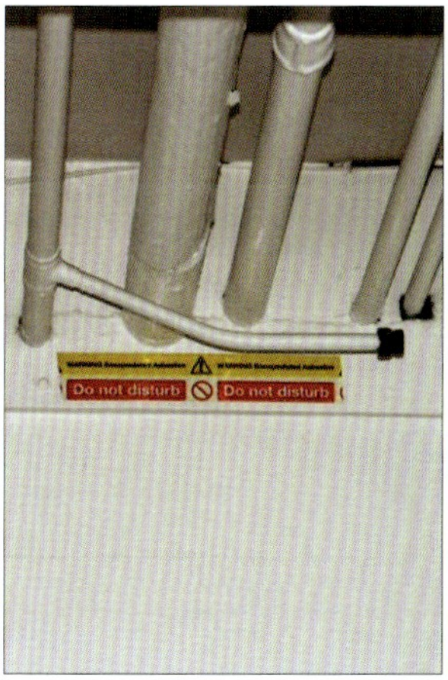

Don't assume there will always be warning signs. There could be undiscovered asbestos in buildings you work on

Asbestos sticks in your lungs. The younger you are, the longer it remains to cause damage

em2 asbestos essentials

Non-licensed tasks

- Asbestos fibres can cause lung cancer and lung diseases.
- Read the safety checklist.
- You must be trained to work safely with asbestos materials.
- Young workers are at special risk due to lack of experience.

INFORMATION

- For information on training providers – see 'More help'.

Information for others

- Tell all other workers that may be nearby what you are doing, where and why.
- Tell them about other risks from the work, eg changes in fire exits.

Training

Equipment and method sheet

What this sheet covers

People that carry out any work on asbestos materials must be trained and supervised properly. You need training even if you worked with asbestos in the past.

Training, supervision and information

- Training must include detailed information on:
  - recognising asbestos;
  - how asbestos can affect your health;
  - the added dangers of smoking;
  - the uses and likely locations for asbestos in buildings;
  - what work you are allowed to do by law;
  - what the law requires you to do;
  - procedures to protect yourself;
  - what methods to use;
  - what equipment you need to do the job properly;
  - how to choose, use and look after personal protective equipment;
  - recognising and dealing with other dangers, such as work at height;
  - decontamination of yourself and work areas;
  - emergency procedures; and
  - waste disposal.
- Refresher training is needed every year, or more often if:
  - work methods change;
  - the type of equipment used changes; or
  - the type of work changes a lot.
- Supervise the task – make sure workers follow the rules.

em3 asbestos essentials

Non-licensed tasks

- **Asbestos fibres can cause lung cancer and lung diseases.**
- **Plan carefully – do you need an HSE licence to do this work?**

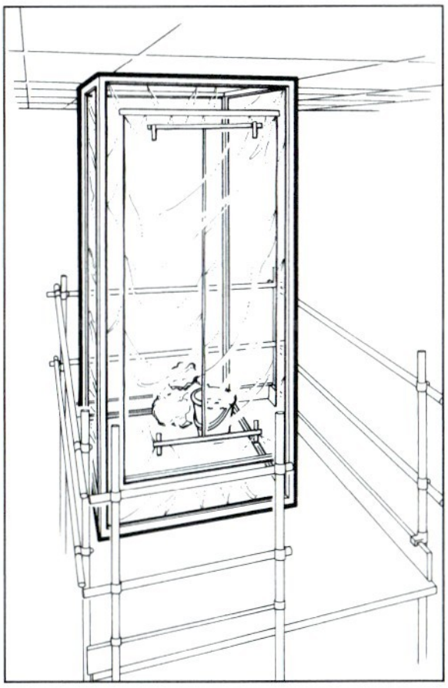

CAUTION

Never use duct tape or spray adhesive on AIB. This will cause damage during dismantling.

Building and dismantling a mini-enclosure

Equipment and method sheet

What this sheet covers

This sheet describes how to build a mini-enclosure. It applies to minor work with asbestos insulating board (AIB). It does not apply to building full enclosures for work that must be carried out by an HSE-licensed contractor.

Caution: A 'mini-enclosure' only prevents asbestos spreading. It does not prevent or control exposures while you are doing the task.

Equipment

- A proprietary 'mini-enclosure', or a home-made 'mini-enclosure' using 1000-gauge polythene sheeting, duct tape and masking tape, and timber or other materials for the frame
- Smoke tubes
- Sealant, eg Polyvinyl acetate (PVA)
- Garden type sprayer
- Bucket of water
- Rags for wiping
- Class H vacuum cleaner (BS 8520) – see sheet em4
- Asbestos waste container, eg labelled polythene sack

Preparing the work area

- Ensure safe access.
- Close doors. Use warning tape or notices to alert other people.

Test the enclosure for leaks with a smoke test

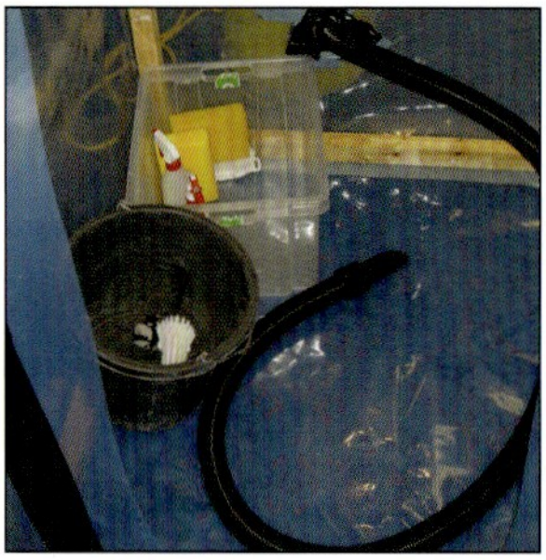

Put the equipment you need inside the enclosure before you start

INFORMATION

Information for others

- Tell all other workers that may be nearby what you are doing, where and why.
- Tell them about other risks from the work, eg changes in fire exits.

Building the enclosure

- Where possible, use a proprietary mini-enclosure as these are quicker and easier to erect – see 'More help'.
- Alternatively, use timber or other materials to build a frame.
- Make the enclosure large enough to do the work safely.
- Attach the polythene sheeting inside the frame with duct tape. This minimises cleaning.
- Attach the polythene sheeting to the ceiling with masking tape only. Attach it to non-asbestos surfaces with duct tape.
- Make an entry slit in one wall of the enclosure and reinforce this with duct tape.
- Attach a polythene sheet above the entry slit, to cover it.
- Check all enclosures for leaks with smoke tubes.
- Release smoke at the seals inside the enclosure. Someone else must check for leaks outside.
- Seal all leaks.
- Put all tools for the task – bucket of water, rags, sprayer, vacuum cleaner nozzle and hose, etc inside the enclosure.

Enclosure dismantling

- Work carefully - prevent asbestos escaping.
- Clean the enclosed area with the Class H vacuum cleaner.
- Clean the equipment and polythene sheeting with damp rags.
- Decontaminate yourself – see sheet em8.
- Inspect the enclosure visually – is it properly clean?
- Spray the polythene sheeting with PVA sealant.
- Remove the sheeting from the framework and put it in the asbestos waste container.
- Remove your protective equipment and dispose of it.
- Tape the container closed. Put it in a clear bag with an asbestos sign.
- If the framework is clean and was fully protected, you can re-use it.

em4 asbestos essentials

Non-licensed tasks

Remember:

- Asbestos fibres can cause lung cancer and lung diseases.
- Check that the vacuum cleaner is in good working order before you start.

Using a Class H vacuum cleaner for asbestos

Equipment and method sheet

What this sheet covers

This sheet describes the Class H vacuum cleaner, how to use it to minimise asbestos fibres released during a task, and how to use it to clean contaminated items.
The cleaner must comply with British Standards.

Never use domestic vacuum cleaners, even those fitted with HEPA (high efficiency particle arrestor) filters.

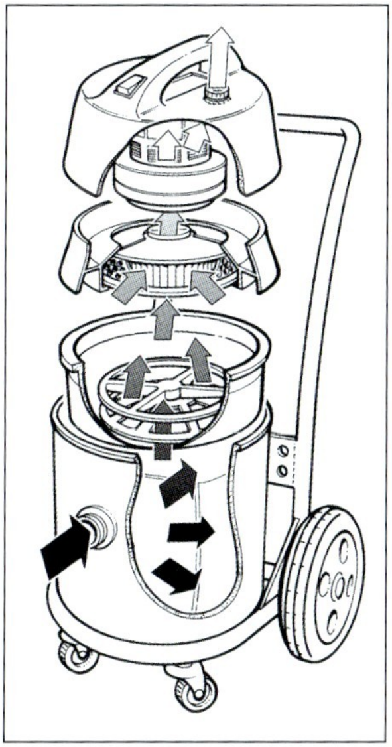

Class H vacuum cleaner

The brush attachment is useful for cleaning protective clothing that might otherwise tear. Decontaminate it after use and bag it for next time

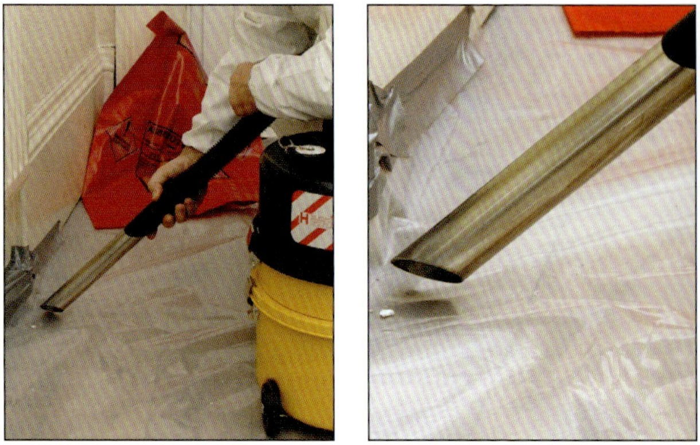

Vacuum clean carefully. It is easy to disturb asbestos fibres, make them airborne and breathe them in

Equipment

- You can hire a Class H vacuum cleaner with a range of attachments; look up 'asbestos safety equipment hire' on the internet, or see 'More help'.
- Ensure hired cleaners are clean and in good working order on receipt.
- The hire company should thoroughly examine and test the cleaner at least once every six months. They need to be licensed by HSE to do this.

Procedures

Vacuuming

- Pick up bigger pieces of debris and put them in a suitable waste container.
- Vacuum clean with care; it is easy to disturb asbestos fibres, make them airborne and breathe them in.
- Wet material can damage the HEPA filter.
- Clean floors, carpets and fabrics with the adjustable floor attachment.
- Clean areas of limited access with the tapered attachment.
- Clean solid surfaces such as desk tops with the flat attachment.
- Check for damage after use.

CAUTION

Avoid using brush attachments for area cleaning. Brushes are difficult to clean properly.

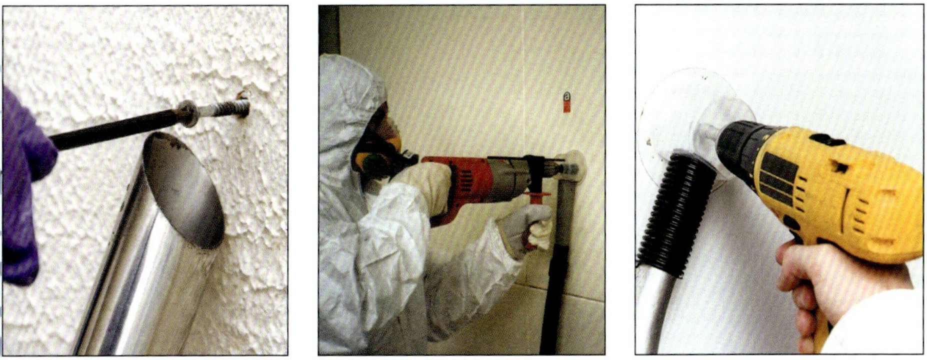

Control measures: shadow vacuuming and using plastic enclosures as local extraction

Used as a control measure – dust extraction

- You can use the Class H vacuum cleaner to control asbestos fibres 'at source', eg:
  - shadow vacuuming: hold the nozzle close to the task (eg screw removal); and
  - local dust extraction at the cutting point: enclose the tool (eg drill bit) with a cowl and attach the nozzle.

Possible problems

- Reduced suction:
  - you have a long extension cable, resulting in low supply voltage;
  - the waste container is full; or
  - the hose has blocked. Clearing it can release asbestos; clear it carefully or get help from the hire company.

Emptying and cleaning

- Follow the hire company's instructions for waste disposal.
- Never clean inside the vacuum cleaner yourself.
- After each use, clean the vacuum cleaner's outer casing and attachments with the vacuum and then with damp rags.
- Inspect the case, hose and attachments visually.
- Keep the hose and attachments in a labelled plastic sack.
- Replace the sealing cap over the hose opening in the cleaner's casing.

CAUTION

You, and other people, will be exposed to high levels of asbestos fibres if you fail to take the proper precautions.

British Standards

You should only hire a Class H vacuum cleaner that conforms to the following standards. For more information on British Standards, see 'Further information'.

- BS 8520-3:2009 *Equipment used in the controlled removal of asbestos-containing materials*. Gives recommendations for the operation, cleaning and maintenance of class H (high hazard) vacuum cleaners containing a filter conforming to BS EN 1822 in the controlled removal of asbestos-containing materials (ACM). It does not apply to any other types of vacuum cleaner for vacuuming up liquids or other applications.

There are many makes of Class H vacuum cleaner. Hire one from a licensed hire company and follow all the instructions. Make sure it conforms to BS 8520-3:2009 and contains a filter conforming to BS EN 1822

em5
asbestos essentials
Non-licensed tasks

Wetting asbestos materials

Equipment and method sheet

What this sheet covers

This sheet explains why you must wet asbestos materials before working on them, and how to do this.
The spraying technique can also be used when painting or sealing asbestos materials.

Damp asbestos materials release far fewer asbestos fibres into the air. Don't drench them and create a waste 'slurry'.

Electrical equipment in the area needs to be isolated and protected.

Equipment

- Wetting agent – for suppliers, see 'More help', or you could use liquid detergent as an alternative
- Sprayer, either a garden type spray or a low pressure spraying machine less than 3.4 bar (50 psi)
- Brush or roller

Procedures

- Wet the asbestos materials before starting any work. Don't work on dry asbestos materials.
- Wetting agents make work easier. Note, blue and brown asbestos don't absorb water easily.
- Some asbestos materials, eg board, sheet cannot be wetted all the way through. So, you need other methods to control dust exposure, eg a Class H vacuum cleaner.

CAUTION

Some tasks will be carried out at height. Make sure that wetting does not create a slipping risk.

Spray at low pressure; high pressure spray could disturb fibres from asbestos paper under these tiles

Sometimes it may be easier to wet the area using a brush or roller

Over-wetting the material creates a waste slurry which will be difficult to clean up

- Vacuuming up very wet material will damage the cleaner's HEPA filter.

Wetting

- Spraying is the preferred wetting method.
- If you use a brush or roller, dispose of it as asbestos waste.
- Dilute the wetting agent with water according to the manufacturer's instructions. This is usually:
  - 10 –15 parts water to 1 part wetting agent; or
  - 8 parts water to 1 part liquid detergent.
- Allow the spray to 'fall' onto the asbestos material – not hit it as a jet.
- Spray carefully; use a slow backwards and forwards motion. Avoid concentrating on any one area – this can disturb the asbestos material or leave dry patches.

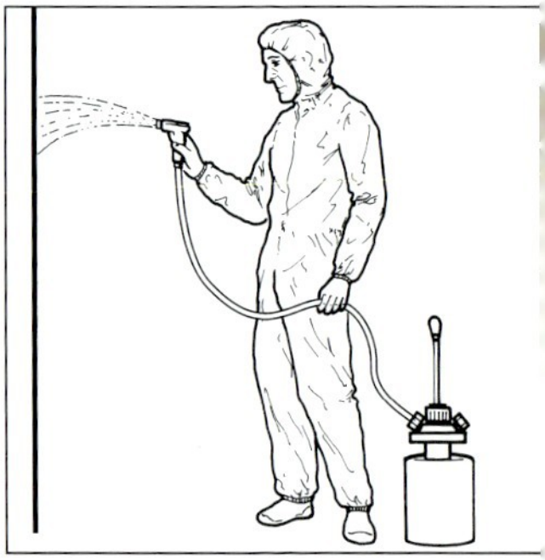

em6
asbestos essentials
Non-licensed tasks

Personal protective equipment (PPE)

Equipment and method sheet

Make sure you use the right PPE for the task

What this sheet covers

This sheet describes what personal protective equipment (PPE) you need.
It also describes respiratory protective equipment (RPE).

PPE and RPE are your last lines of defence against asbestos fibres. Follow the methods in the task guidance sheets to avoid fibres being released into the air.

Overalls

- Disposable overalls. Type 5 (BS EN ISO 13982-1) are suitable. Cotton overalls hold dust and need specialist laundering.
- You may need waterproof overalls for outdoor work.
- Wear one size too big - this will help to prevent ripping at the seams.
- If the cuffs are loose, seal them with tape.
- Avoid wearing a long-sleeved shirt – these are difficult to cover properly.
- Wear the overall legs over footwear. Tucking them in lets dust into footwear.
- Wear the hood over the RPE straps.
- Dispose of used overalls as asbestos waste.

Gloves

- If you wear protective gloves, use single-use disposable gloves. If you must use latex gloves, use only 'low protein powder-free' gloves.

If you must use latex gloves, use only 'low protein powder-free' gloves

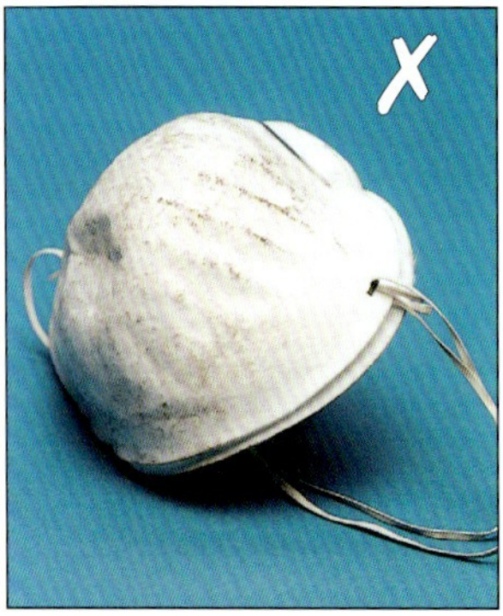

A 'dust mask' doubled up for more protection is useless. You need a respirator

CAUTION

- **Never use laced boots, these are very difficult to clean properly.**
- **Never take used overalls home.**

- Dispose of used gloves as asbestos waste.

Footwear

- Boots are preferable to disposable overshoes which cause a slipping risk.

Respiratory protective equipment (RPE)

- Use suitable RPE with an Assigned Protection Factor of 20 or more.
- Suitable types of RPE:
  - disposable respirator to standards EN149 (type FFP3) or EN1827 (type FMP3);
  - half mask respirator (to standard EN140) with P3 filter; or
  - semi-disposable respirator (to EN405) with P3 filter.
- This equipment should be suitable for most short duration non-licensed work. Workers should select a make and size that fits them.
- This equipment is **not** suitable for people with beards or stubble, or for long periods of continuous use; you need powered equipment for such situations.

Planning and preparation

- Plan for and practice emergency procedures.
- Workers need to be fit tested to make sure that the RPE fits them properly.
- Arrange fit testing and training before the work starts, ask the supplier for help or contact BOHS (www.bohs.org). Also see 'More help'.
- Workers must be medically fit to wear RPE – seek medical advice if you are not sure.

Using RPE

- All types of RPE restrict what the wearer can do. It is uncomfortable to wear for long periods.
- The RPE has to be worn all the time and until the worker is away from the contaminated air.
- Put on and wear the respirator in accordance with the manufacturer's instructions.

- Place the straps firmly around the top and back of the head. The respirator should be tight against the face.
- When using disposable RPE, pinch the top of the respirator over the nose.
- Carry out a fit check in accordance with the manufacturer's instructions.
- If the worker wears spectacles, they should put them on now. They must not create a gap between the mask and face.
- Put the overall hood over the straps.
- At the end of the shift, take off RPE last and, if it is disposable, put it in the asbestos waste. If it is any other type, decontaminate, clean and store it properly for the next use.
- With half-mask type change filters regularly – your supplier may be able to advise you how often. Dispose of used filters as asbestos waste.

Maintenance of non-disposable equipment

- Keep RPE clean and in good working order – follow the manufacturer's instructions.
- Inspect and check RPE for damage every time. Carry out thorough checks monthly (or every three months if used infrequently). Inspect all parts including valves and seals. Replace the respirator as appropriate.
- Clean RPE after use and store in a safe place away from contamination.

For some tasks, non-disposable RPE is needed

Training

- Make sure that RPE users know:
  - how to check their equipment is working properly before they put it on;
  - how to check that it fits;
  - how to identify and replace worn or defective parts; and
  - that they know about the limitations of the RPE they are using.
- Instruct users to throw away disposable RPE/PPE as asbestos waste after one use.
- Tell workers to stop work and leave the area if they think their RPE is not working properly.

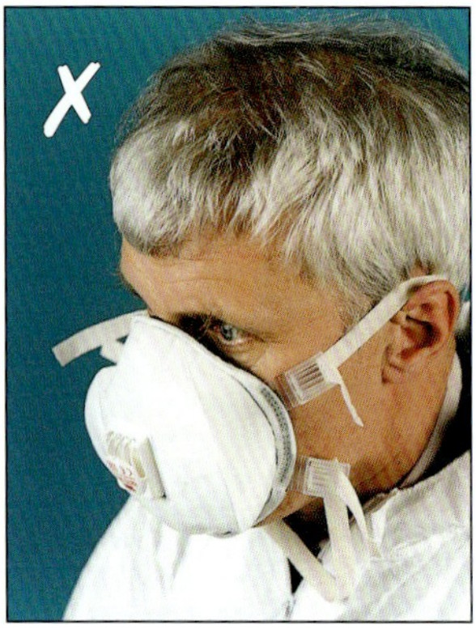

Disposable RPE worn incorrectly

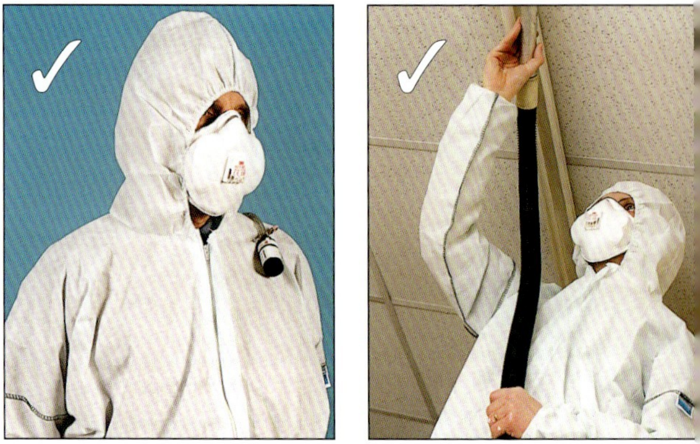

Disposable RPE worn correctly

Further information

- *Asbestos: The licensed contractors' guide* HSG247 HSE Books 2006 ISBN 978 0 7176 2874 2
- *Respiratory protective equipment at work: A practical guide* HSG53 (Third edition) HSE Books 2005 ISBN 978 0 7176 2904 6
- *Fit testing of respiratory protective equipment facepieces* HSE Information Operational Circular OC 282/28 www.hse.gov.uk/foi/internalops/fod/oc/200-299/282_28.pdf

CAUTION

- **Never leave the respirator lying around where it can collect dust. Never dangle the respirator round your neck.**
- **Make sure the correct filter is fitted.**

em7
asbestos essentials
Non-licensed tasks

Using damp rags to clean surfaces of minor asbestos contamination

Equipment and method sheet

What this sheet covers

This sheet explains how to use rags to clean minor asbestos contamination from smooth, non-absorbent surfaces and equipment.

Equipment

- Bucket of water
- Either cotton rags that do not shed fluff onto clean surfaces, or impregnated rags (eg 'Tak' rags)
- Adhesive tape, to collect small dust deposits
- Asbestos waste container, eg labelled polythene sack

Procedures

- Pick up bigger pieces of debris and put them in a suitable waste container.

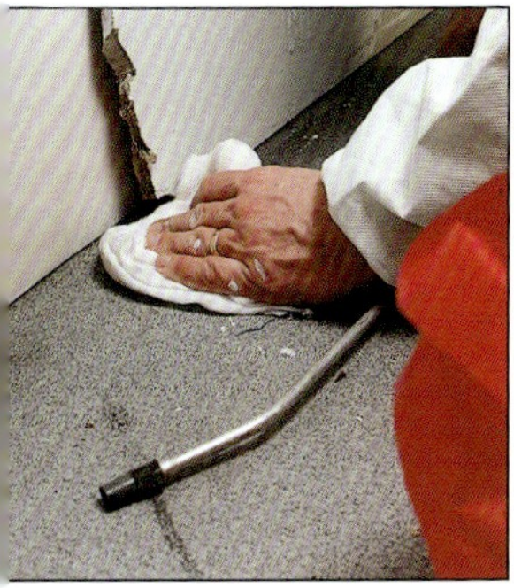

Wiping up debris with a damp rag

Rags

- Impregnated rags do not need soaking.
- Soak the rag in water. Fold in half or quarters. Wring it out.
- Wipe the contaminated surface.
- Re-fold the rag to give a clean surface.
- Repeat until you have used all the clean surfaces of the rag.
- Put the used rag in a bag. Get a clean rag, and repeat cleaning until all surfaces are clean.

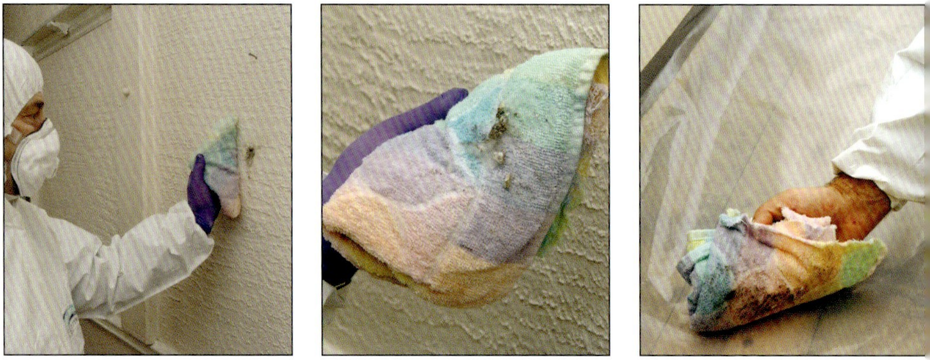

Re-fold the rag between wiping, and dispose of it once all of its clean surfaces have been used

Tape

- Tape is useful only for removing small dust deposits. Surfaces may need repeated tape applications.
- Place a strip of tape over the contaminated surface. Peel it off slowly.
- Put the used tape in a bag. Repeat with a fresh piece.

Wastes

- Put bags of used rags and tape in a suitable asbestos waste container.
- Tape the container closed.
- If you avoid contaminating the bucket of water, no special precautions are need for water disposal.
- See sheet em9 for disposal.

CAUTION

Never re-soak a contaminated rag. This contaminates the water.

em8

asbestos essentials

Non-licensed tasks

Personal decontamination

Equipment and method sheet

What this sheet covers

This sheet describes how to decontaminate yourself after any work with asbestos materials.
Personal decontamination is easier when you wear the correct personal protective equipment (PPE).

You need to decontaminate yourself properly, otherwise you may take asbestos fibres home on your clothing and expose your family and friends.

Procedures

Removing and decontaminating personal protective equipment (PPE)

- Clean your boots with damp rags – see sheet em7.
- Where available, clean your overalls with the brush attachment on a Class H vacuum cleaner. Vacuum off the brush.

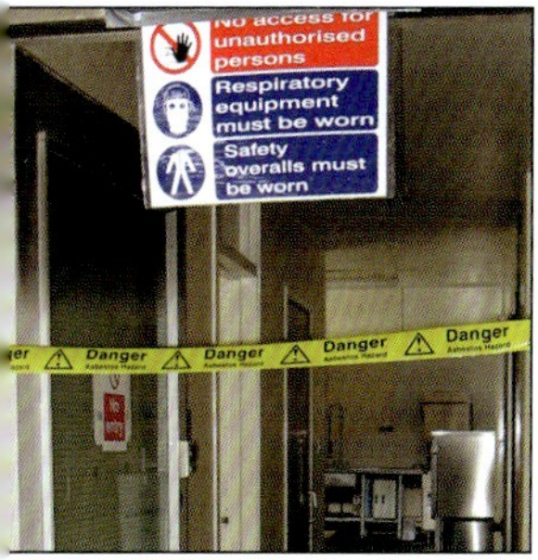

Make sure you restrict access

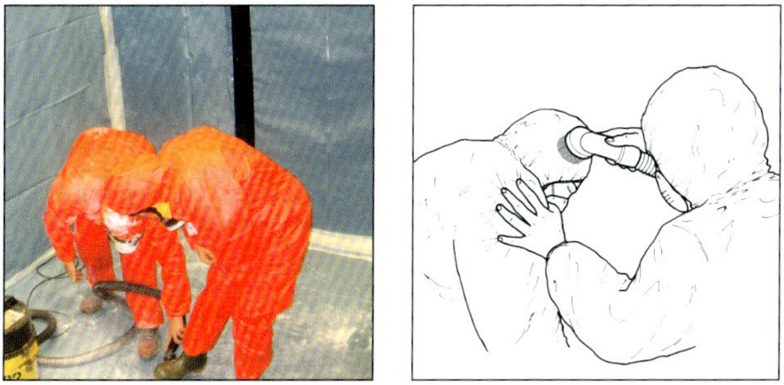

'Buddy' cleaning using a Class H vacuum cleaner

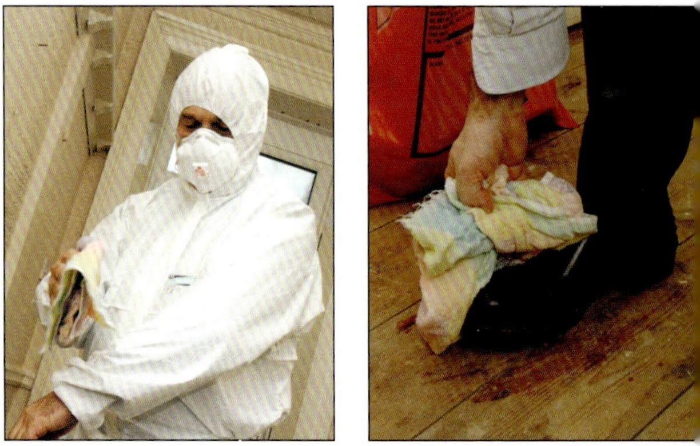

With damp rags, use a patting action to avoid disturbing fibres

- Otherwise, use damp rags by a 'patting' action. Rubbing can disturb fibres.
- Where there are two workers, they can help to clean each other.
- Peel off disposable overalls. They should be inside out. Put them in a suitable asbestos waste container.
- Bag up re-usable overalls for a specialist laundry.
- Finally, remove your disposable respirator and place it in the asbestos waste container.
- Tape the container closed.

Personal decontamination

- Can you use site washing facilities? If so, they must be for your use only.
- Keep other people out during personal decontamination, and until you have cleaned the facilities.
- Wash every time you leave the work area.
- Use damp rags to clean the washing facilities at the end of the job.
- Clean the facilities daily if the job lasts more than one day.
- Inspect the facilities visually once the job is finished.
- Clearance air sampling is not normally needed for washing facilities.

em9 asbestos essentials

Non-licensed tasks

Disposal of asbestos waste

Equipment and method sheet

> **CAUTION**
>
> Don't overfill bags. Beware of sharp objects that could puncture plastic.

Vehicle placard

What this sheet covers

This sheet describes good practice when you need to dispose of asbestos waste.

Any asbestos product or material that is ready for disposal is defined as asbestos waste. Asbestos waste also includes contaminated building materials, tools that cannot be decontaminated, personal protective equipment and damp rags used for cleaning. If in doubt, always treat waste as 'Hazardous' or 'Special'. See the table for more details.

You can discharge waste water that may be contaminated with traces of asbestos to the sewage system.

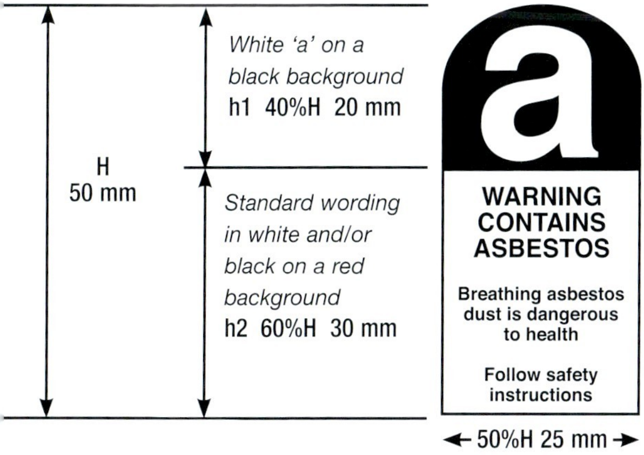

All waste should be double-bagged or double-wrapped in plastic sheeting, with the correct hazard warning signs attached

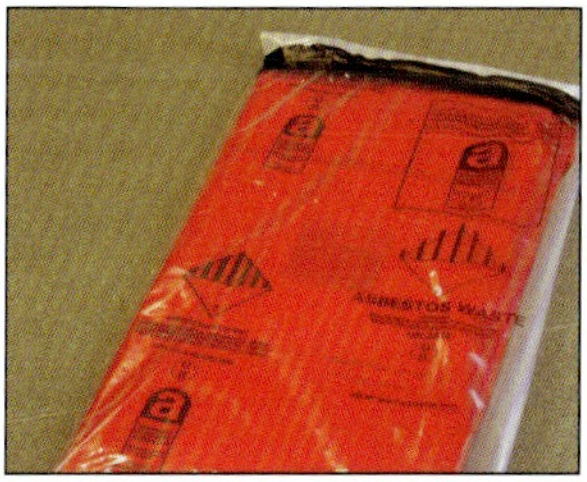

England and Wales	■ Asbestos waste is 'Hazardous Waste' when it contains more than 0.1% asbestos. ■ The Hazardous Waste Regulations apply. Complete a Waste Consignment Note. ■ Contact the Environment Agency for more information.
Scotland	■ Asbestos waste is 'Special Waste' when it contains more than 0.1% asbestos. ■ The Special Waste Amendment (Scotland) Regulations apply. Complete a Waste Consignment Note. ■ Contact the Scottish Environment Protection Agency for more information.
England, Scotland and Wales	■ All asbestos waste is subject to Schedule 2 of the Control of Asbestos Regulations 2012 and most waste is subject to the Carriage of Dangerous Goods (etc) Regulations 2009 (CDG 2009). ■ Firmly-bound asbestos – asbestos cement and articles with asbestos reinforcement – does not release hazardous or respirable fibres easily. CDG does not apply. ■ The Carriage of Dangerous Goods (etc) Regulations 2009 (CDG 2009) applies for all other asbestos waste – see 'More help'.

Caution: Don't mix asbestos waste with other waste to get below 0.1%.

Use a lockable skip for asbestos cement sheets. It is not good enough to throw sheeting over a standard skip

- Waste must be packed in UN-approved packaging with a CDG hazard sign and asbestos code information visible.
- Double-wrap and label asbestos waste. Standard practice is to use a red inner bag with asbestos warnings, and a clear outer bag with the CDG sign.
- If you carry waste, use a sealed skip, or a vehicle with the following:
  - segregated compartment for asbestos;
  - easily cleanable; and
  - lockable.
- Otherwise, arrange for transport by a registered waste carr
- Safe disposal – at a licensed disposal site.
- Complete a Waste Consignment Note. Keep copies of these documents for three years.

Further information

- *Asbestos: The licensed contractors' guide* HSG247 HSE Books 2006 ISBN 978 0 7176 2874 2

em10
asbestos essentials
Non-licensed tasks

Statement of cleanliness after textured coating removal

Equipment and method sheet

What this sheet covers

This sheet is intended for trained contractors who remove textured coatings.
It sets out a model statement to issue to the client, premises owner or the occupier.

- After removing textured coating, you need to let the client know the premises are safe to use again.
- Before you do this you need to be sure that textured coating has been removed as agreed, and all debris cleaned up.
- The next page shows an example of a form to give to the client, premises owner or occupier.

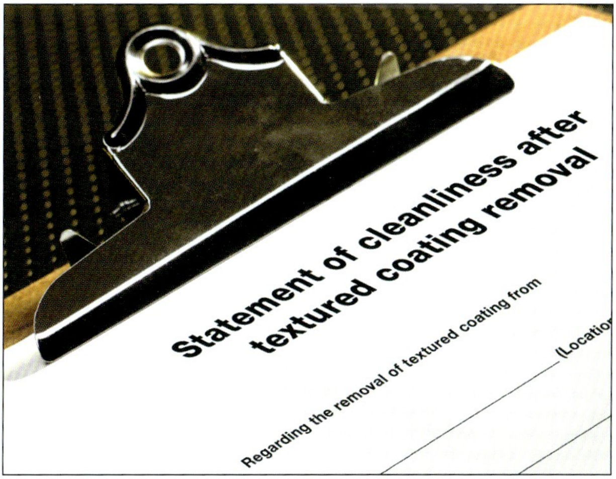

Regarding the removal of textured coating from:

____ (Location)

____ (Address)

____

____

on: ____ (Date)

The removal work consisted of:

____

____ (Job description)

by: ____ (Name of contractor)

____

____

____ (Contractor's address)

I have checked that textured coating was removed and the area was cleaned thoroughly. I inspected the following areas to make sure that there were no visible traces of dust or debris:

____

____

____

____

____ (Areas inspected)

I am satisfied that the area can be returned to normal use.

Signed: ____________________ Name: ____________________ (capitals)

Date: ____________________

a1 asbestos essentials

Non-licensed tasks

ESSENTIAL INFORMATION

Also read the following sheets in this book:

em1 (p11) *What to do if you uncover or damage materials that may contain asbestos*

em2 (p14) *Training*

em4 (p17) *Using a Class H vacuum cleaner for asbestos*

em6 (p23) *Personal protective equipment (PPE)*

em7 (p27) *Using damp rags to clean surfaces of minor asbestos contamination*

em8 (p29) *Personal decontamination*

em9 (p31) *Disposal of asbestos waste*

Drilling holes in asbestos insulating board (AIB)

What this sheet covers

This sheet describes good practice when you need to drill into AIB to attach fittings, or to pass through cables or pipework.

This sheet is NOT appropriate if work lasts more than one hour per week for a worker, or two hours in total for two or more workers; use an HSE-licensed contractor for such work.

Preparing the work area

- Ensure safe access.
- Restrict access – minimise the number of people present.
- Close doors. Use tape and notices to warn others.
- If feasible, also restrict general access to the rear of the AIB.
- If this is not possible, warn the building owner that this area is contaminated.
- Ensure adequate lighting.

Equipment

- 500-gauge polythene sheeting and duct tape
- Warning tape and notices
- Class H vacuum cleaner (BS 8520) – see sheet em4
- Drill – manual or powered, set at the lowest speed
- Drill bit, or hole cutter for holes greater than 20 mm diameter
- Plastic enclosure for vacuum cleaner nozzle, to extract around the drill bit

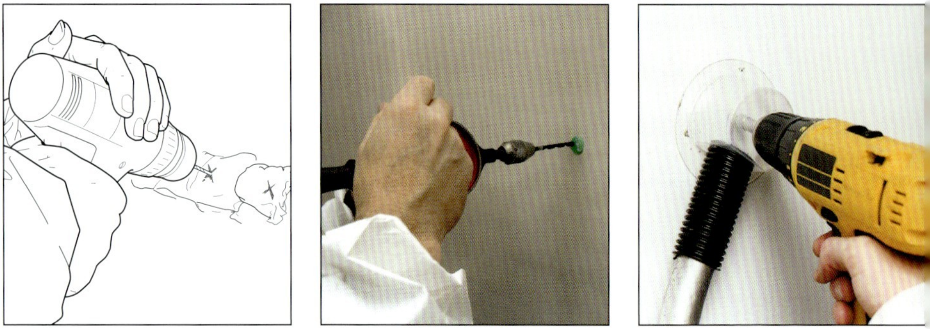

Drill through paste or foam or use a plastic cowl and a Class H vacuum cleaner. A hand drill creates less dust. If you have to use an electric drill, put it on the slowest setting

- Masking tape
- Thick paste, eg wallpaper paste or shaving foam, or a proprietary device to contain drilling debris
- Permanent sealant
- Plastic or metal sleeve to protect hole edges
- Bucket of water and rags
- Asbestos waste container, eg labelled polythene sack
- Clear polythene sack

Personal protective equipment (PPE) – see sheet em6

- Provide:
  - disposable overalls fitted with a hood;
  - boots without laces (laced boots are hard to decontaminate); and
  - respiratory protective equipment.

Procedure

- Protect nearby surfaces from contamination. Cover with 500-gauge polythene sheeting and fix with duct tape to non-asbestos surfaces.
- Cover the drilling point and the rear (if accessible) with masking tape to prevent the edges crumbling.
- For cable and pipework, make the hole slightly bigger than required.

OTHER HAZARDS

Work at height – see www.hse.gov.uk/falls/index.htm. Take precautions to avoid falls. Must you work from a ladder? Where necessary, erect an access platform.

There may be other hazards – you need to consider them all.

Method 1: Drilling 1 to 5 holes up to 20 mm in diameter in board less than 6 mm thick

- Cover the drill entry and if accessible, exit points, with a generous amount of paste, foam or a proprietary device.
- Drill through the paste, foam or device.
- Clean off the paste, foam and debris with damp rags. Or remove the device and clean the surface. Clean the back surface with damp rags, if accessible.
- Rags and paste or foam contain dust and fibres. Dispose of as asbestos waste.
- Seal the drilled edge with sealant.
- Insert a sleeve to protect the hole's edges from cabling etc.

Method 2: Drilling 6 to 20 holes, or any hole over 20 mm in diameter, or drilling through board more than 6 mm thick.

- Place the plastic enclosure over the drill point. Put the drill bit or cutter through the enclosure opening.
- Attach the Class H vacuum cleaner hose to the plastic enclosure. Turn it on.
- Drill the hole.
- Vacuum the drilled hole, and the rear of the board if accessible.
- Seal the drilled edge with sealant.
- Insert a sleeve to protect the hole's edges.

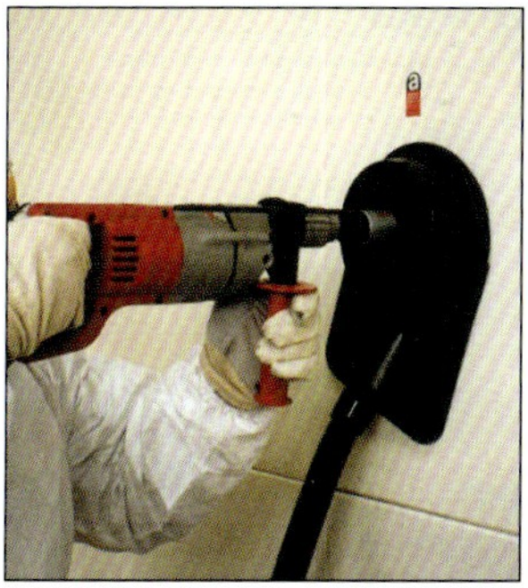

Control measures: Shadow vacuuming and using plastic enclosures as local extraction

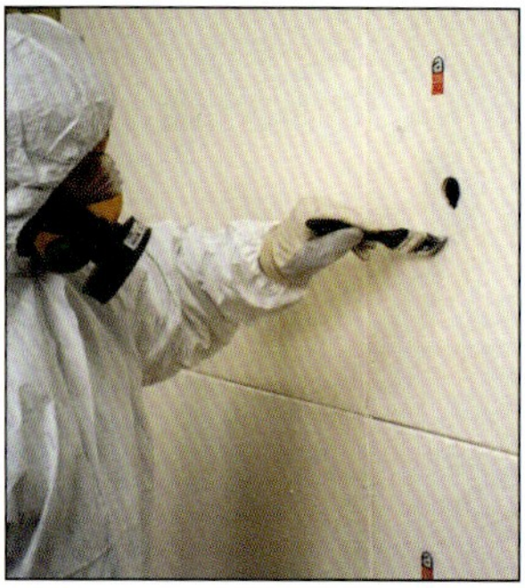

Seal the drilled edge with sealant

Cleaning and disposal

- Clean the equipment and the area with the Class H vacuum cleaner and/or damp rags.
- Put used rags, polythene sheeting and other waste in the asbestos waste container and tape it closed.
- Put the asbestos waste container in a clear polythene sack and tape it closed.
- Disposal – see sheet em9.

Personal decontamination

- See sheet em8.

Clearance and checking off

- Visually inspect the area to make sure that it has been cleaned properly.
- Clearance air sampling is not normally required.
- Get the premises owner, dutyholder or client to check off the job.

a2 asbestos essentials

Non-licensed tasks

ESSENTIAL INFORMATION

Also read the following sheets in this book:

em1 (p11) *What to do if you uncover or damage materials that may contain asbestos*

em2 (p14) *Training*

em3 (p15) *Building and dismantling a mini-enclosure*

em4 (p17) *Using a Class H vacuum cleaner for asbestos*

em5 (p21) *Wetting asbestos materials*

em6 (p23) *Personal protective equipment (PPE)*

em7 (p27) *Using damp rags to clean surfaces of minor asbestos contamination*

em8 (p29) *Personal decontamination*

em9 (p31) *Disposal of asbestos waste*

Removing a single (screwed-in) asbestos insulating board (AIB) ceiling tile

What this sheet covers

This sheet describes good practice when you need to remove a single AIB ceiling tile.

This sheet is NOT appropriate:

- **for the removal of AIB slats;**
- **where the tile has more than minor damage;**
- **where the tile is heavily painted so its removal could damage adjacent tiles; or**
- **if work lasts more than one hour per week for a worker, or two hours in total for two or more workers; (this includes time to set up, dismantle and clean the mini-enclosure).**

Use an HSE-licensed contractor for such work.

Preparing the work area

- Ensure safe access.
- Restrict access – minimise the number of people present.
- Close doors. Use tape and notices to warn others.
- Ensure adequate lighting.

Equipment

- Method 1: 500-gauge polythene sheeting and duct tape
- Method 2: use a mini-enclosure if available – if not, use timber or other framework with 1000-gauge polythene sheeting and duct tape – see sheet em3
- 1000-gauge polythene sheeting and duct tape

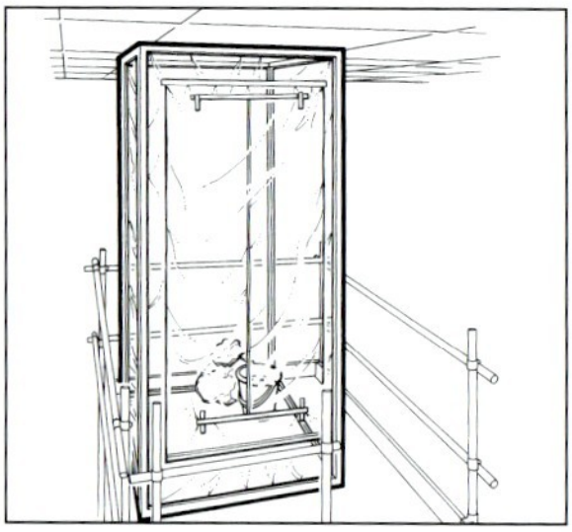

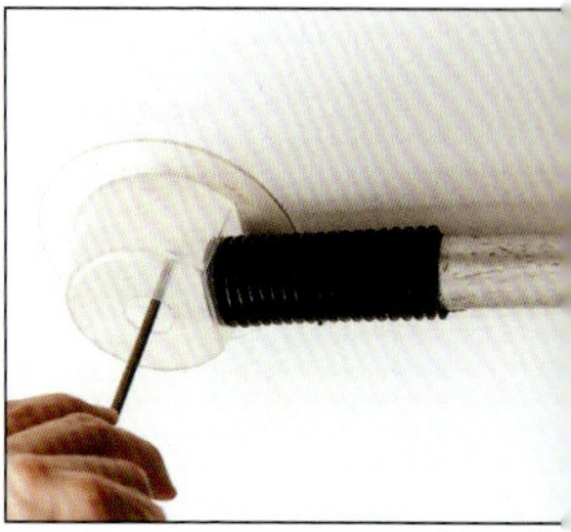

Protect nearby areas with polythene sheeting or a mini-enclosure. Use shadow vacuuming to control dust when removing screws

- Warning tape and notices
- Class H vacuum cleaner (BS 8520) – see sheet em4
- Sealant, eg polyvinyl acetate (PVA)
- Magnet
- Screwdriver
- Non-asbestos replacement ceiling tile
- Garden-type sprayer containing wetting agent
- Bucket of water and rags
- Asbestos waste container, eg labelled polythene sack
- Clear polythene sack

Personal protective equipment (PPE) – see sheet em6

- Provide:
  - disposable overalls fitted with a hood;
  - boots without laces (laced boots are hard to decontaminate); and
  - respiratory protective equipment.

Method 1: Removing a single ceiling tile less than 0.36 square metres in area (eg 60 cm x 60 cm)

Procedure

- Protect nearby surfaces from contamination. Cover with 500-gauge polythene sheeting and fix with duct tape to non-asbestos surfaces.

Removal

- Locate steel screws with the magnet. Locate brass

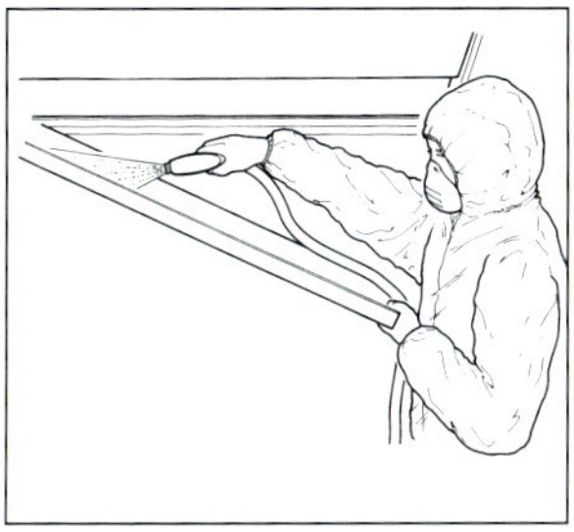

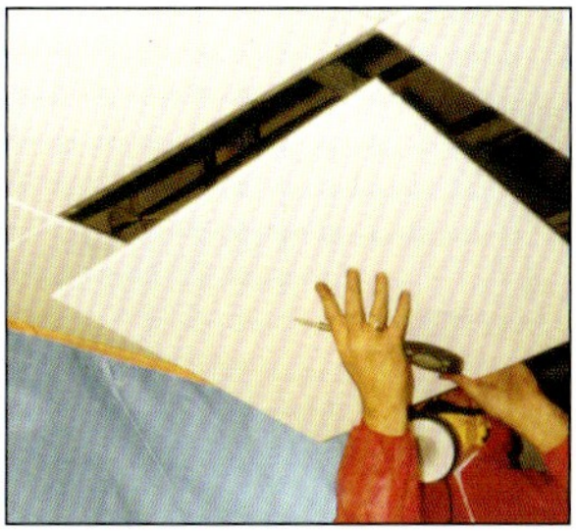

Carefully lower one end of the tile. Vacuum its upper surface and spray with PVA. Keep the tile flat and lower it gently

screws by careful paint scraping.

- Use 'shadow vacuuming' to control dust – see sheet em4.
- Unscrew – put the screws in the waste container.
- Carefully lower one end of the tile. Vacuum its upper surface.
- Spray the upper surface with PVA.
- Keep the tile flat and lower it gently.
- Place the tile in the asbestos waste container.
- If asbestos fillets are present, seal with a sealant.
- Fix a new non-asbestos tile by attaching it to a non-asbestos surface, not to asbestos fillets.

Method 2: Removing a single ceiling tile more than 0.36 square metres in area (eg 60 cm x 60 cm)

Procedure

- Erect a proprietary 'mini-enclosure', or build one as described in sheet em3.

Removal

- Follow the removal instructions for method 1.
- Double-wrap the tile in 1000-gauge polythene sheeting.

OTHER HAZARDS

Work at height – see www.hse.gov.uk/falls/ index.htm. Take precautions to avoid falls. Must you work from a ladder? Where necessary, erect an access platform.

Manual handling – see www.hse.gov.uk/msd/index.htm. Plan how to remove and handle heavy material and articles safely.

There may be other hazards – you need to consider them all.

Cleaning and disposal

- Clean a mini-enclosure with the Class H vacuum cleaner and dismantle it as advised in sheet em3.
- Clean the area and equipment with the Class H vacuum cleaner and damp rags.
- Put used rags, polythene sheeting and other waste in the asbestos waste container and tape it closed.
- Put the asbestos waste container in a clear polythene sack and tape it closed.
- Disposal – see sheet em9.

Personal decontamination

- See sheet em8.

Clearance and checking off

- Visually inspect the area to make sure that it has been cleaned properly.
- Clearance air sampling is not normally required.
- Get the premises owner, dutyholder or client to check off the job.

a3

asbestos essentials

Non-licensed tasks

Removing a door with asbestos insulating board (AIB) fireproofing

ESSENTIAL INFORMATION

Also read the following sheets in this book:

em1 (p11) *What to do if you uncover or damage materials that may contain asbestos*

em2 (p14) *Training*

em5 (p21) *Wetting asbestos materials*

em7 (p27) *Using damp rags to clean surfaces of minor asbestos contamination*

em8 (p29) *Personal decontamination*

em9 (p31) *Disposal of asbestos waste*

What this sheet covers

This sheet describes good practice when you need to dispose of a door backed with AIB. It is also suitable where AIB is sandwiched within the door.

This sheet is NOT appropriate:

- **for the removal of an AIB panel (see sheet a4); or**
- **for the disposal of a door with more than minor damage to the AIB.**

Use an HSE-licensed contractor for such work.

Preparing the work area

- Restrict access – minimise the number of people present.
- Close doors. Use tape and notices to warn others.
- Ensure adequate lighting.

Equipment

- 1000-gauge polythene sheeting and duct tape
- Warning tape and notices
- Sealant, eg polyvinyl acetate (PVA)
- Screwdriver
- Non-asbestos replacement fire door
- Garden-type sprayer containing wetting agent, eg diluted washing-up liquid
- Bucket of water and rags
- Asbestos waste container, eg labelled polythene sack
- Clear polythene sack
- Asbestos warning stickers

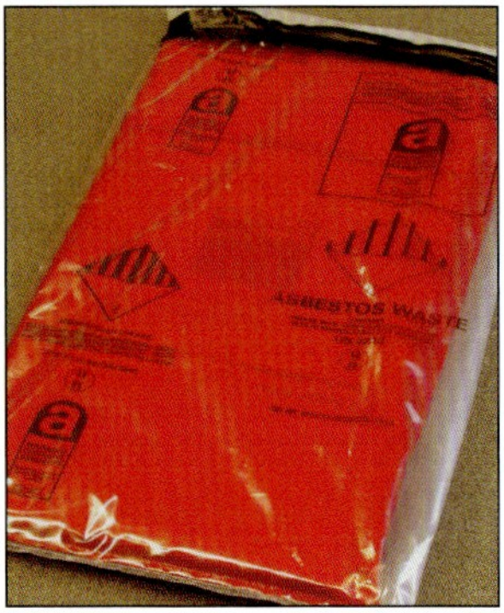

Double wrap the door in polythene sheeting with asbestos warning stickers

Personal protective equipment (PPE)

- Provide:
  - disposable overalls fitted with a hood;
  - boots without laces (laced boots are hard to decontaminate).
- A respirator is not normally required.

Procedure

- If unpainted, spray the board with PVA sealant.
- If the board is within the door, spray all exposed edges.
- Allow it to dry.
- Lay enough polythene sheeting on the floor to wrap up the door.
- Unscrew the door from its hinges and lower it onto the polythene sheet.
- Double-wrap the door with polythene sheeting and secure with duct tape.
- Attach asbestos warning stickers.
- If necessary, fit a replacement door with the same fire protection properties.

Cleaning and disposal

- Clean the equipment and area with damp rags.
- Put debris, used rags, polythene sheeting and other waste in the asbestos waste container and tape it closed.
- Put the asbestos waste container in a clear polythene sack and tape it closed.
- Disposal – see sheet em9.

Personal decontamination

- See sheet em8.

Clearance and checking off

- Visually inspect the area to make sure that it has been cleaned properly.
- Clearance air sampling is not normally required.
- Get the premises owner, dutyholder or client to check off the job.

OTHER HAZARDS

Manual handling – see www.hse.gov.uk/msd/index.htm. Plan how to remove and handle heavy material and articles safely.

There may be other hazards – you need to consider them all.

a4 asbestos essentials

Non-licensed tasks

Removing a single asbestos insulation board (AIB) panel, less than 1m^2, fixed with nails or screws

ESSENTIAL INFORMATION

Also read the following sheets in this book:

em1 (p11) *What to do if you uncover or damage materials that may contain asbestos*

em2 (p14) *Training*

em3 (p15) *Building and dismantling a mini-enclosure*

em4 (p17) *Using a Class H vacuum cleaner for asbestos*

em5 (p21) *Wetting asbestos materials*

em6 (p23) *Personal protective equipment (PPE)*

em7 (p27) *Using damp rags to clean surfaces of minor asbestos contamination*

em8 (p29) *Personal decontamination*

em9 (p31) *Disposal of asbestos waste*

What this sheet covers

This sheet describes good practice when you need to remove a single AIB sheet less than 1 square metre in area.
This sheet is NOT appropriate:

- **when the AIB has more than minor damage or is heavily painted so its removal could damage adjacent panels;**
- **when the AIB is in the form of ceiling tiles or slats;**
- **for removing heavily nailed or centre-nailed panels;**
- **for soffits;**
- **for a panel larger than 1 square metre; or**
- **for removing more than two small panels a week.**

Use an HSE-licensed contractor for such work.

Preparing the work area

- Ensure safe access
- Restrict access – minimise the number of people present
- Close doors. Use tape and notices to warn others
- Ensure adequate lighting

Equipment

- 500- and 1000-gauge polythene sheeting and duct tape
- Warning tape and notices
- Class H vacuum cleaner (BS 8520) – see sheet em4
- Thick paste, eg wallpaper paste or shaving foam

CAUTION

If the panel has nails in the centre, the job needs an HSE-licensed contractor.

- Sealant, eg polyvinyl acetate (PVA)
- Permanent sealant
- Magnet
- Screwdriver
- Garden-type sprayer containing wetting agent
- Paint brush
- Bucket of water and rags
- Asbestos waste container, eg labelled polythene sack
- Asbestos warning stickers
- Clear polythene sack

Personal protective equipment (PPE) – see sheet em6

- Provide:
  - disposable overalls fitted with a hood;
  - boots without laces (laced boots are hard to decontaminate); and
  - respiratory protective equipment.

Procedure

- Inspect carefully. If the AIB is in good condition and is unlikely to get damaged upon removal, follow this sheet.
- If the board is badly damaged or likely to get damaged, use an HSE-licensed contractor.

Panel with nails

- Erect a mini-enclosure – see sheet em3.
- If you can remove nails with the claw, do so with ‘shadow vacuuming’ – see sheet em4.
- If this is not possible, you need to break the panel across one corner. Cover the intended break line with paste/foam.
- Deeply score the panel across one nailed corner through the paste/foam.
- Lever to break the panel at the scored line – hold the vacuum nozzle near to the break to collect as much dust as possible.
- Ease the panel away to loosen other nails, and remove these with shadow vacuuming.
- Remove the panel and vacuum all newly-exposed surfaces.

Use a mini-enclosure if you need to remove a panel fixed with nails

Panel with screws

- Protect nearby surfaces from contamination. Cover with 500-gauge polythene sheeting and fix with duct tape to non-asbestos surfaces.
- Locate steel screws with the magnet. Locate brass screws by careful paint scraping.
- Use 'shadow vacuuming' to control dust – see sheet em4.
- Unscrew – put the screws in the waste container.
- Ease the panel away. Vacuum its newly-exposed surfaces and screw holes.

All panels

- Spray the panel with PVA.
- Double-wrap large panels with 1000-gauge polythene sheeting; place smaller boards in the waste container.
- Attach asbestos warning stickers.
- Gently paint newly-exposed surfaces and screw holes with sealant paint.

Cleaning and disposal

- Clean any newly-exposed surfaces with the Class H vacuum cleaner.
- Clean a mini-enclosure with the Class H vacuum cleaner and dismantle it as advised in sheet em3.

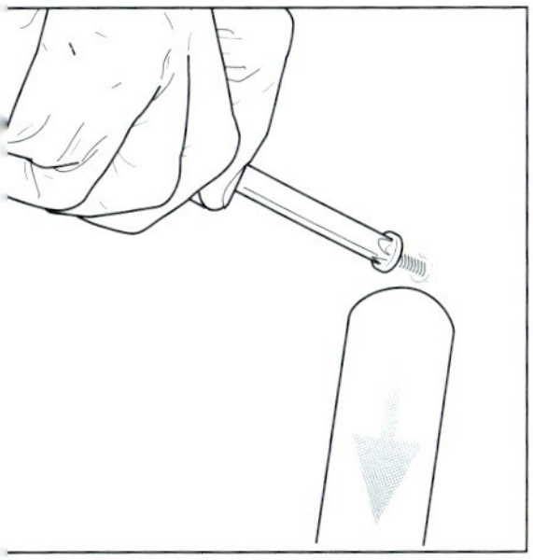

Panel with screws: Use shadow vacuuming to control dust as you remove screws

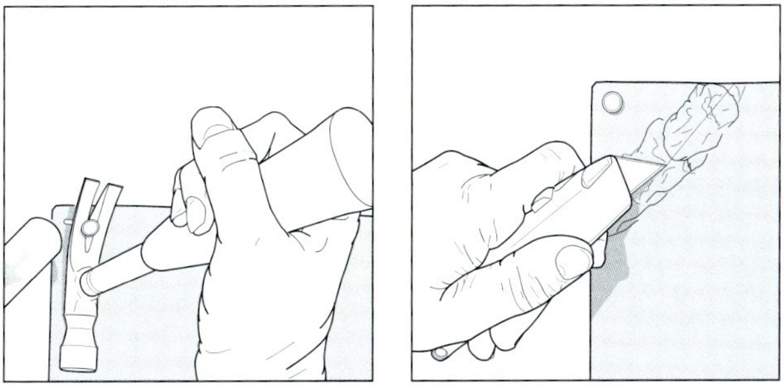

Panel with nails: If possible, remove nails with a claw and shadow vacuuming. If this is difficult without damaging the board, apply paste to one corner and make a deep score line so you can lever the corner away first

OTHER HAZARDS

Work at height – see www.hse.gov.uk/falls/index.htm. Take precautions to avoid falls. Must you work from a ladder? Where necessary, erect an access platform.

Manual handling – see www.hse.gov.uk/msd/index.htm. Plan how to remove and handle heavy material and articles safely.

There may be other hazards – you need to consider them all.

- Clean the area and equipment with the Class H vacuum cleaner and damp rags.
- Put debris, used rags, polythene sheeting, paintbrush and other waste in the asbestos waste container and tape it closed.
- Put the asbestos waste container in a clear polythene sack and tape it closed.
- Disposal – see sheet em9.

Personal decontamination

- See sheet em8.

Clearance and checking off

- Visually inspect the area to make sure that it has been cleaned properly.
- Clearance air sampling is not normally required.
- Get the premises owner, dutyholder or client to check off the job.

a5
asbestos essentials
Non-licensed tasks

Cleaning light fittings attached to asbestos insulating board (AIB)

ESSENTIAL INFORMATION

Also read the following sheets in this book:

em1 (p11) *What to do if you uncover or damage materials that may contain asbestos*

em2 (p14) *Training*

em4 (p17) *Using a Class H vacuum cleaner for asbestos*

em6 (p23) *Personal protective equipment (PPE)*

em7 (p27) *Using damp rags to clean surfaces of minor asbestos contamination*

em8 (p29) *Personal decontamination*

em9 (p31) *Disposal of asbestos waste*

What this sheet covers

This sheet describes good practice when you need to clean a contaminated light fitting attached to AIB, eg to change a bulb or tube.

This sheet is NOT appropriate where the AIB is damaged, or may be damaged eg by 'rocking' the screws during cleaning. Use an HSE-licensed contractor for such work.

See sheet em4 *Using a Class H vacuum cleaner for asbestos* when removing a screwed in fitting, and sheet a6 for minor damage repair.

Preparing the work area

- Ensure safe access.
- Restrict access – minimise the number of people present.
- Close doors. Use tape and notices to warn others.
- Ensure adequate lighting.

Equipment

- 500-gauge polythene sheeting and duct tape
- Warning tape and notices
- Class H vacuum cleaner (BS 8520) – see sheet em4
- Bucket of water and rags
- Asbestos waste container, eg labelled polythene sack
- Clear polythene sack

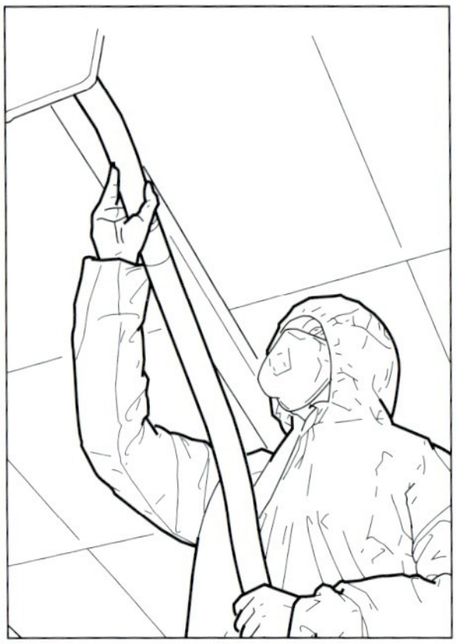

Cleaning inside the tube fitting with a Class H vacuum cleaner

OTHER HAZARDS

Work at height – see www.hse.gov.uk/falls/index.htm. Take precautions to avoid falls. Must you work from a ladder? Where necessary, erect an access platform.

Electrical hazards – see www.hse.gov.uk/electricity/index.htm. Get a competent electrician to isolate and reconnect electricity supply.

There may be other hazards – you need to consider them all.

Personal protective equipment (PPE) – see sheet em6

- Provide:
  - disposable overalls fitted with a hood;
  - boots without laces (laced boots are hard to decontaminate); and
  - respiratory protective equipment.

Procedure

- Isolate the power supply – use a competent electrician.
- Protect nearby surfaces from contamination. Cover with 500-gauge polythene sheeting and fix with duct tape to non-asbestos surfaces.
- Avoid removing the light fitting – this may disturb the AIB.
- Clean the light fitting exterior with the Class H vacuum cleaner.
- Place easily removable sections on the polythene sheeting, for cleaning on the floor.
- Open the light fitting carefully. Insert the Class H vacuum cleaner hose, and clean inside the fitting.
- Complete the cleaning with the Class H vacuum cleaner.

Cleaning and disposal

- Clean the area with damp rags.
- Put debris, used rags, polythene sheeting and other waste in the asbestos waste container and tape it closed.
- Put the asbestos waste container in a clear polythene sack and tape it closed.
- Disposal – see sheet em9.

Personal decontamination

- See sheet em8.

Clearance and checking off

- Visually inspect the area to make sure that it has been cleaned properly.
- Clearance air sampling is not normally required.
- Get the premises owner, dutyholder or client to check off the job.

a6

asbestos essentials

Non-licensed tasks

ESSENTIAL INFORMATION

Also read the following sheets in this book:

em1 (p11) *What to do if you uncover or damage materials that may contain asbestos*

em2 (p14) *Training*

em6 (p23) *Personal protective equipment (PPE)*

em7 (p27) *Using damp rags to clean surfaces of minor asbestos contamination*

em8 (p29) *Personal decontamination*

em9 (p31) *Disposal of asbestos waste*

This damaged AIB needs to be covered and protected from further damage

Repairing minor damage to asbestos insulating board (AIB)

What this sheet covers

This sheet describes good practice when you need to repair small areas of damaged AIB, eg a broken corner or scratches. This sheet is NOT appropriate:

- **if work lasts more than one hour per week for a worker, or two hours in total for two or more workers; or**
- **where the material is badly damaged.**

Use an HSE-licensed contractor for such work.

If AIB is in a position where further damage is likely, see sheet a8.

Preparing the work area

- Ensure safe access.
- Restrict access – minimise the number of people present.
- Close doors. Use tape and notices to warn others.
- Ensure adequate lighting.

Equipment

- 500-gauge polythene sheeting and duct tape
- Warning tape and notices
- Liquid impact adhesive
- Permanent sealant
- Non-asbestos covering panel
- Garden-type sprayer or small paint brush
- Bucket of water and rags
- Asbestos waste container, eg labelled polythene sack
- Clear polythene sack

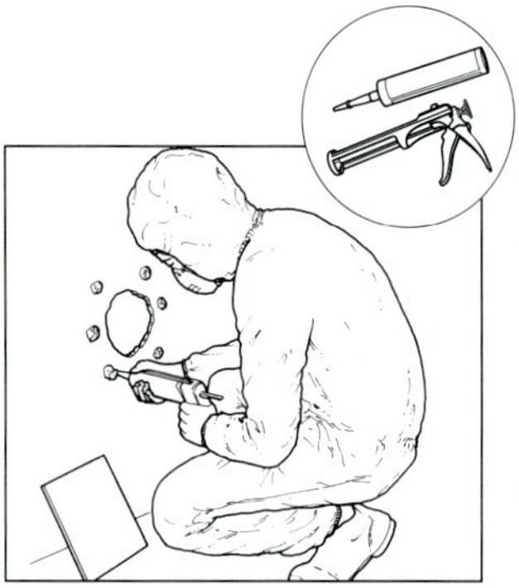

Attach the replacement panel with adhesive

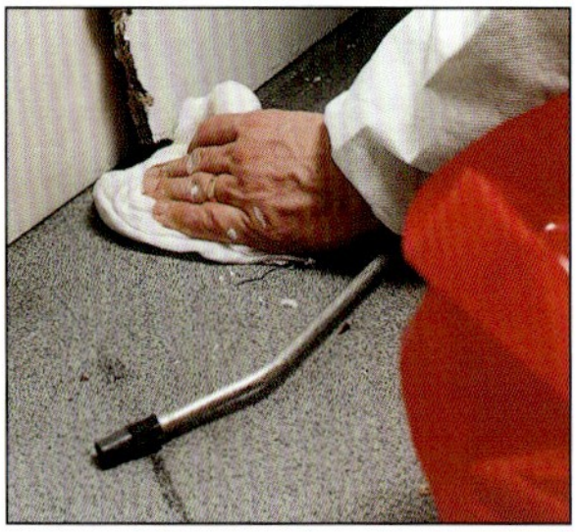

Wipe up dust and debris with a damp rag

OTHER HAZARDS

Work at height – see www.hse.gov.uk/falls/ index.htm. Take precautions to avoid falls. Must you work from a ladder? Where necessary, erect an access platform.

There may be other hazards – you need to consider them all.

Personal protective equipment (PPE) - see sheet em6

- Provide:
  - disposable overalls fitted with a hood;
  - boots without laces (laced boots are hard to decontaminate); and
  - respiratory protective equipment.

Procedure

- Protect nearby surfaces from contamination. Cover with 500-gauge polythene sheeting and fix with duct tape to non-asbestos surfaces.
- Remove small bits of loose board – use a damp rag. Put these in the waste container.
- Paint the damaged area with sealant by brush or gentle spraying.
- After drying, cover gaps with the replacement panel. Attach it with adhesive.
- Wipe dusty surfaces with a damp rag.

Cleaning and disposal

- Clean the equipment and the area with damp rags.
- Put debris, used rags, polythene sheeting and other waste in the asbestos waste container and tape it closed.
- Also dispose of the used paint brush.
- Put the asbestos waste container in a clear polythene sack and tape it closed.
- Disposal – see sheet em9.

Personal decontamination

- See sheet em8.

Clearance and checking off

- Visually inspect the area to make sure that it has been cleaned properly.
- Clearance air sampling is not normally required.
- Get the premises owner, dutyholder or client to check off the job.

a7 asbestos essentials

Non-licensed tasks

ESSENTIAL INFORMATION

Also read the following sheets in this book:

em1 (p11) *What to do if you uncover or damage materials that may contain asbestos*

em2 (p14) *Training*

em4 (p17) *Using a Class H vacuum cleaner for asbestos*

em7 (p27) *Using damp rags to clean surfaces of minor asbestos contamination*

em8 (p29) *Personal decontamination*

em9 (p31) *Disposal of asbestos waste*

CAUTION

Never prepare surfaces by sanding or rubbing down.

Painting undamaged asbestos insulating board (AIB)

What this sheet covers

This sheet describes good practice when you need to paint undamaged AIB for protection or for decoration.

This sheet is NOT appropriate where the asbestos material is badly damaged. Use an HSE-licensed contractor for such work.

Preparing the work area

- Ensure safe access.
- Restrict access – minimise the number of people present.
- Close doors. Use tape and notices to warn others.
- Ensure adequate lighting.

Equipment

- 500-gauge polythene sheeting and duct tape
- Warning tape and notices
- Class H vacuum cleaner (BS 8520 – see sheet em4) if dust needs to be removed from AIB
- Low-solvent paint
- Low-pressure sprayer, brush or roller
- Bucket of water and rags
- Asbestos waste container, eg labelled polythene sack
- Clear polythene sack

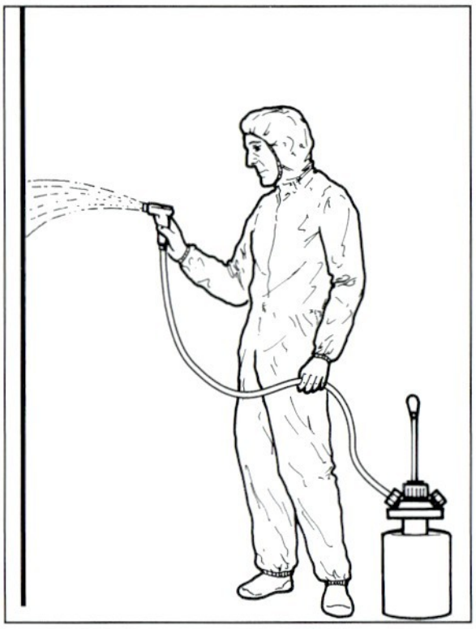

Use low-pressure spraying where possible

Personal protective equipment (PPE)

- Provide
  - disposable overalls fitted with a hood; and
  - boots without laces (laced boots are hard to decontaminate).
- A respirator is not normally required

Procedure

- Check that there is no damage before starting work; if there is, see sheet a6.
- Protect nearby surfaces from contamination. Cover with 500-gauge polythene sheeting and fix with duct tape to non-asbestos surfaces.
- Remove dust using the Class H vacuum cleaner.
- Apply the paint, preferably by low-pressure spraying. Spray using a sweeping motion.
- If painting by brush or roller, do so gently and avoid concentrating on one area, to reduce surface damage.

Cleaning and disposal

- Clean the equipment and the area with damp rags.
- Put debris, used rags, polythene sheeting, paintbrush/ roller and other waste in the asbestos waste container and tape it closed.
- Put the asbestos waste container in a clear polythene sack and tape it closed.
- Disposal – see sheet em9.

Personal decontamination

- See sheet em8.

Clearance and checking off

- Visually inspect the area to make sure that it has been cleaned properly.
- Clearance air sampling is not normally required.
- Get the premises owner, dutyholder or client to check off the job.

OTHER HAZARDS

Work at height – see www.hse.gov.uk/falls/index.htm. Take precautions to avoid falls. Must you work from a ladder? Where necessary, erect an access platform.

There may be other hazards – you need to consider them all.

a8

asbestos essentials

Non-licensed tasks

Enclosing undamaged asbestos materials to prevent impact damage

ESSENTIAL INFORMATION

Also read the following sheets in this book:

em1 (p11) *What to do if you uncover or damage materials that may contain asbestos*

em2 (p14) *Training*

em7 (p27) *Using damp rags to clean surfaces of minor asbestos contamination*

em8 (p29) *Personal decontamination*

em9 (p31) *Disposal of asbestos waste*

What this sheet covers

This sheet describes good practice when you need to protect asbestos materials from impact damage, and you do not want to remove them. Examples include:

- **asbestos insulating board wall panels that could be damaged by trolleys; or**
- **lagged pipework running along the bottom of a wall that could be scuffed.**

For minor repairs on asbestos insulating board see sheet a6. For minor repairs on asbestos cement see sheet a13.

This sheet is NOT appropriate where the asbestos material is badly damaged or where you disturb the asbestos. Use an HSE-licensed contractor for such work.

Preparing the work area

- Restrict access – minimise the number of people present.
- Close doors. Use tape and notices to warn others.
- Ensure adequate lighting.

Equipment

- Warning tape and notices
- Liquid impact adhesive
- Screwdriver
- Nails or screws
- Hammer

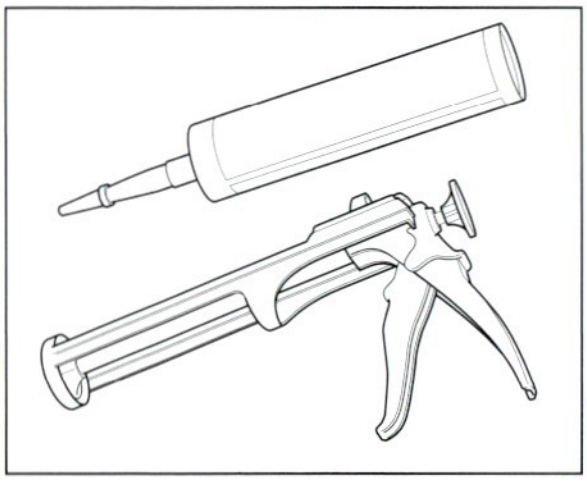

If you have to attach panels to asbestos-containing materials, use impact adhesive

Use non-asbestos boarding to protect asbestos

OTHER HAZARDS

Work at height – see www.hse.gov.uk/falls/index.htm. Take precautions to avoid falls. Must you work from a ladder? Where necessary, erect an access platform.

There may be other hazards – you need to consider them all.

- Non-asbestos board – this may need to meet an original specification, eg fire resistant
- Bucket of water and rags
- Asbestos waste container, eg labelled polythene sack
- Clear polythene sack

Personal protective equipment (PPE)

- Provide:
  - disposable overalls fitted with a hood; and
  - boots without laces (laced boots are hard to decontaminat
- A respirator is not normally required.

Procedure

- Box-in pipework without disturbing the asbestos.
- Where possible, fix replacement panels to non-asbestos materials – you can use nails or screws.
- Use adhesive to attach replacement panels to asbestos-containing materials.
- Seal the cavity and provide adequate fire barriers.
- Warn the building owner about the presence of asbestos-containing material, so it can be managed properly.

Cleaning and disposal

- Clean the equipment and the area with damp rags.
- Put debris, used rags and other waste in the asbestos waste container and tape it closed.
- Put the asbestos waste container in a clear polythene sack and tape it closed.
- Disposal – see sheet em9.

Personal decontamination

- See sheet em8.

Clearance and checking off

- Visually inspect the area to make sure that it has been cleaned properly.
- Clearance air sampling is not normally required.
- Get the premises owner, dutyholder or client to check off the job.

a9

asbestos essentials

Non-licensed tasks

Drilling holes in asbestos cement (AC) and other highly bonded materials

ESSENTIAL INFORMATION

Also read the following sheets in this book:

em1 (p11) *What to do if you uncover or damage materials that may contain asbestos*

em2 (p14) *Training*

em6 (p23) *Personal protective equipment (PPE)*

em7 (p27) *Using damp rags to clean surfaces of minor asbestos contamination*

em8 (p29) *Personal decontamination*

em9 (p31) *Disposal of asbestos waste*

What this sheet covers

This sheet describes good practice when you need to drill holes in asbestos cement, bitumen products, floor tiles or other highly-bonded materials containing asbestos.
For asbestos insulating board, see sheet a1.
For textured coatings, see sheet a26.

Preparing the work area

- Ensure safe access.
- Restrict access – minimise the number of people present.
- Close doors. Use tape and notices to warn others.
- If feasible, also restrict access to the rear of asbestos material. If drilling a roof from outside, segregate the area beneath.
- If access to the rear is not possible, warn the building owner that this area is contaminated.
- Ensure adequate lighting.

Asbestos cement tiles on a roof

Interior floor tiles

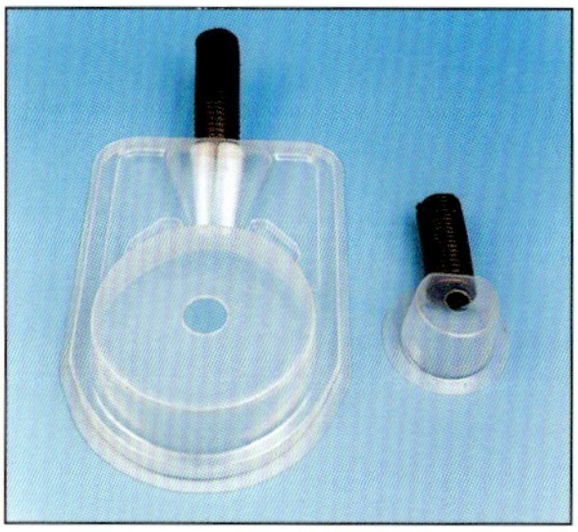

Proprietary device to contain drilling debris

Use a hole cutter, for holes greater than 20 mm

Equipment

- 500-gauge polythene sheeting and duct tape
- Warning tape and notices
- Drill – manual or powered, set at the lowest speed
- Drill bit, or hole cutter for holes greater than 20 mm diameter
- Masking tape
- Thick paste, eg wallpaper paste or shaving foam, or a proprietary device to contain drilling debris
- Mastic or sealant for gaps
- Plastic or metal sleeve to protect hole edges
- Bucket of water and rags
- Asbestos waste container, eg labelled polythene sack
- Clear polythene sack

Personal protective equipment (PPE) – see sheet em6

- Provide:
  - disposable overalls fitted with a hood;
  - boots without laces (laced boots are hard to decontaminate); and
  - respiratory protective equipment.

Procedure

- Protect nearby surfaces from contamination. Cover with 500-gauge polythene sheeting and fix with duct tape to non-asbestos surfaces.
- Cover the drilling point and the rear (if accessible) with masking tape to prevent the edges crumbling.

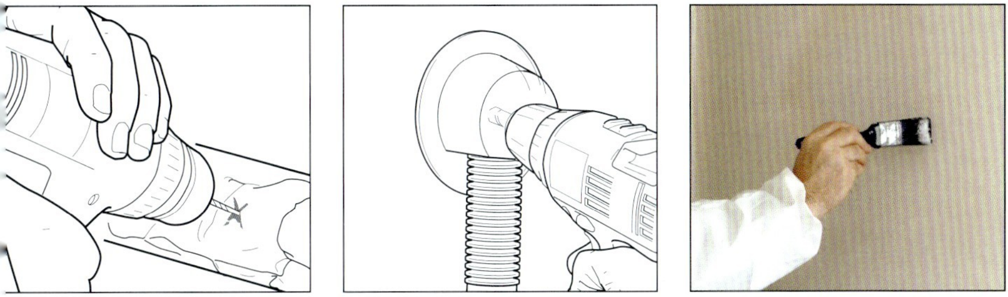

Drill through masking tape covered with paste or foam, or use a cowl connected to a Class H vacuum cleaner as local extraction. Seal drilled edges with sealant

- For cable and pipework, make the hole slightly bigger than required.
- Cover the drill entry and if accessible, exit points, with a generous amount of paste, foam or a proprietary device.
- Drill through the paste, foam or device.
- Clean off the paste, foam and debris with damp rags and remove the masking tape. Or remove the device and clean the surface. Clean the back surface with damp rags, if accessible.
- Rags and paste or foam contain dust and fibres. Dispose of as asbestos waste.
- Seal the drilled edge with sealant.
- Insert a sleeve to protect the hole's edges from cabling etc.

Cleaning and disposal

- Clean the equipment and the area with damp rags.
- Put debris, used rags, polythene sheeting, paintbrush and other waste in the asbestos waste container and tape it closed.
- Put the asbestos waste container in a clear polythene sack and tape it closed.
- Disposal – see sheet em9.

OTHER HAZARDS

Work at height – see www.hse.gov.uk/falls/index.htm. Take precautions to avoid falls. Must you work from a ladder? Where necessary, erect an access platform.

Slips and trips – see www.hse.gov.uk/slips/index.htm. Floors protected with polythene become very slippery when wet.

There may be other hazards – you need to consider them all.

Personal decontamination

- See sheet em8.

Clearance and checking off

- Visually inspect the area to make sure that it has been cleaned properly.
- Clearance air sampling is not normally required.
- Get the premises owner, dutyholder or client to check off the job.

a10
asbestos
essentials
Non-licensed tasks

Cleaning debris from guttering on an asbestos cement (AC) roof

ESSENTIAL INFORMATION

Also read the following sheets in this book:

em1 (p11) *What to do if you uncover or damage materials that may contain asbestos*

em2 (p14) *Training*

em5 (p21) *Wetting asbestos materials*

em7 (p27) *Using damp rags to clean surfaces of minor asbestos contamination*

em8 (p29) *Personal decontamination*

em9 (p31) *Disposal of asbestos waste*

CAUTION

AC roofs are always fragile and cannot bear weight.

What this sheet covers

This sheet describes good practice when you need to remove debris from guttering.
The guttering may be made of AC, or it may simply collect water from an AC roof.

Preparing the work area

- Ensure safe access.
- Can you do this work from ground-level?
- Restrict access – minimise the number of people present.
- Use tape and notices to warn others.

Equipment

- Warning tape and notices
- Scoop, trowel or scraper
- Garden-type sprayer or watering can containing wetting agent
- Bucket of water and rags
- Asbestos waste container, eg labelled polythene sack
- Clear polythene sack

Personal protective equipment (PPE)

- Provide:
  - disposable overalls fitted with a hood;
  - boots without laces (laced boots are hard to decontaminate); and
  - protective gloves. Select single use gloves.

Wet the debris again if you find dry material, avoid creating a slurry

OTHER HAZARDS

Work at height – see www.hse.gov.uk/falls/index.htm. Take precautions to avoid falls. Must you work from a ladder? Where necessary, erect an access platform.

Work on fragile roofs – see www.hse.gov.uk/construction/index.htm. Fragile roofs cannot bear weight.

There may be other hazards – you need to consider them all.

- A respirator is not normally required

Procedure

- Sprinkle the wetting solution into the gutter. Avoid creating a slurry.
- Scoop out the debris into the waste container.
- Wet the debris again if you find dry material.

Cleaning and disposal

- Clean the equipment with damp rags.
- Put used rags and other waste in the asbestos waste container and tape it closed.
- Put the asbestos waste container in a clear polythene sack and tape it closed.
- Disposal – see sheet em9.

Personal decontamination

- See sheet em8.

Clearance and checking off

- Visually inspect the area to make sure that it has been cleaned properly.
- Clearance air sampling is not normally required.
- Get the premises owner, dutyholder or client to check off the job.

a11 asbestos essentials

Non-licensed tasks

ESSENTIAL INFORMATION

Also read the following sheets in this book:

em1 (p11) *What to do if you uncover or damage materials that may contain asbestos*

em2 (p14) *Training*

em5 (p21) *Wetting asbestos materials*

em6 (p23) *Personal protective equipment (PPE)*

em7 (p27) *Using damp rags to clean surfaces of minor asbestos contamination*

em8 (p29) *Personal decontamination*

em9 (p31) *Disposal of asbestos waste*

CAUTION

AC roofs are always fragile and cannot bear weight.

Removing asbestos cement (AC) debris

What this sheet covers

This sheet describes good practice when you need to clear up AC. This includes decontamination following a fire.
This sheet is NOT appropriate for cleaning debris from damaged asbestos lagging, insulation or insulating board. Use an HSE-licensed contractor for such work.

For fly-tipped AC waste, see sheet a38.

Preparing the work area

- Ensure safe access.
- Restrict access – minimise the number of people present.
- Close doors. Use tape and notices to warn others.
- Ensure adequate lighting.

Equipment

- Warning tape and notices
- Scoop, trowel or scraper
- Adhesive tape
- Garden-type sprayer containing wetting agent
- Bucket of water and rags
- Asbestos waste container, eg labelled polythene sack
- Clear polythene sack

Personal protective equipment (PPE) – see sheet em6

- Provide:
  - disposable overalls fitted with a hood; and

- boots without laces (laced boots are hard to decontaminate).

- A respirator is not normally required if there are only a few pieces of contamination in a small area, or the pieces are damp.
- For larger or heavily contaminated areas, a respirator is required.

Procedure

- Clean up visible contamination in occupied areas, eg houses and gardens nearby. In large contaminated areas, eg following a fire, you may be unable to remove all the AC.
- Dampen the AC debris with spray.
- Pick up larger pieces of debris. Put them in the waste container.
- For debris on rough surfaces, keep it damp and scoop or scrape it into the waste container.
- Clean contaminated surfaces with damp rags, then put these in the waste container.
- Press adhesive tape onto small dust deposits, then put the tape in the waste container.
- If necessary, repair the AC – see sheet a13.
- Put used rags and other waste in the asbestos waste container and tape it closed.
- Put the asbestos waste container in a clear polythene sack and tape it closed.
- Disposal – see sheet em9.

Personal decontamination

- See sheet em8.

Clearance and checking off

- Visually inspect the area to make sure that it has been cleaned properly.
- Clearance air sampling is not normally required.
- Get the premises owner, dutyholder or client to check off the job.

AC debris is common

OTHER HAZARDS

Work at height – see www.hse.gov.uk/falls/index.htm. Take precautions to avoid falls. Must you work from a ladder? Where necessary, erect an access platform.

Work on fragile roofs – see www.hse.gov.uk/construction/index.htm. Fragile roofs cannot bear weight.

There may be other hazards – you need to consider them all.

CAUTION

Make sure the debris is AC only.

a12

asbestos essentials

Non-licensed tasks

Cleaning weathered asbestos cement (AC) roofing and cladding

ESSENTIAL INFORMATION

Also read the following sheets in this book:

em1 (p11) *What to do if you uncover or damage materials that may contain asbestos*

em2 (p14) *Training*

em6 (p23) *Personal protective equipment (PPE)*

em7 (p27) *Using damp rags to clean surfaces of minor asbestos contamination*

em8 (p29) *Personal decontamination*

em9 (p31) *Disposal of asbestos waste*

CAUTION

AC roofs are always fragile and cannot bear weight.

What this sheet covers

This sheet describes good practice when you need to clean AC cladding and roofing, either to improve its appearance or to prepare it for a surface coating.
This sheet is NOT appropriate for cleaning asbestos insulating board. Use an HSE-licensed contractor for such work.

Preparing the work area

- Ensure safe access.
- Restrict access – minimise the number of people present.
- Use tape and notices to warn others.

Equipment

- 500-gauge polythene sheeting and duct tape
- Warning tape and notices
- Approved biocide
- Scoop or trowel
- Scraper
- Proprietary cleaning machine
- Garden-type sprayer containing wetting agent
- Bucket of water and rags
- Asbestos waste container, eg labelled polythene sack
- Clear polythene sack

Moss and lichen growth on asbestos cement roofing and gutters

Personal protective equipment (PPE) – see sheet em6

- Provide:
  - disposable overalls fitted with a hood (you may need waterproof overalls);
  - boots without laces (laced boots are hard to decontaminate);
  - protective gloves. Select single use gloves; and
  - a disposable particulate respirator (eg FF P3) for manual scraping and for operating the filtration system.

- A respirator is not normally needed for an operator who is well away from the cleaning machine.

Procedure

- Prevent slurry entering the building. Seal gaps into the building with polythene sheeting, secured with duct tape.
- If necessary, remove debris first – see sheet a11.
- Only in exceptional circumstances is high pressure jetting appropriate. This requires a specialist contractor.

CAUTION

It is dangerous to seal over exhaust vents from gas-fired equipment. Can the equipment be turned off?

Method 1: Cleaning cladding accessible from ground level

- Prepare the biocide according to the instructions on the label. Apply it by low pressure sprayer.
- Allow time for the biocide to work – check the product label.
- Keep the surface wet and remove growths by gentle scraping. Dead plant roots are hard to remove – leave these in place.
- Scoop debris into the waste container.

Method 2: Employ a specialist roof cleaning contractor with a cleaning machine

- This method creates a lot of slurry that must be collected for disposal.
- The contractor should:
  - divert the slurry through a collection and filtration system;
  - keep solid waste wet and put it in the waste container; and
  - flush out the slurry collector with clean water.

Cleaning and disposal

- Clean the equipment and the area with damp rags.
- Put debris, used rags, polythene sheeting, paintbrush and other waste in the asbestos waste container and tape it closed.

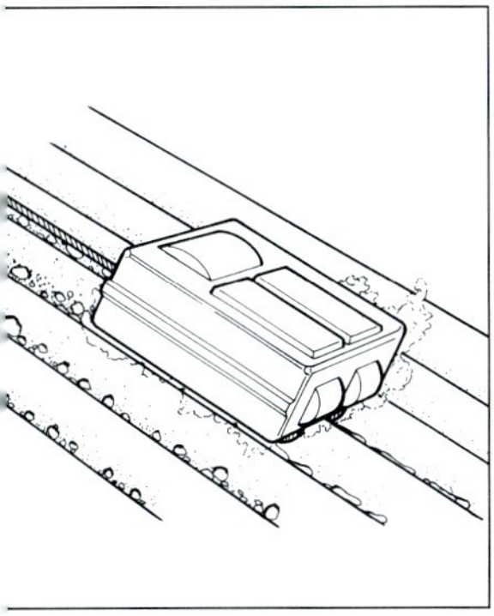

Cleaning machine

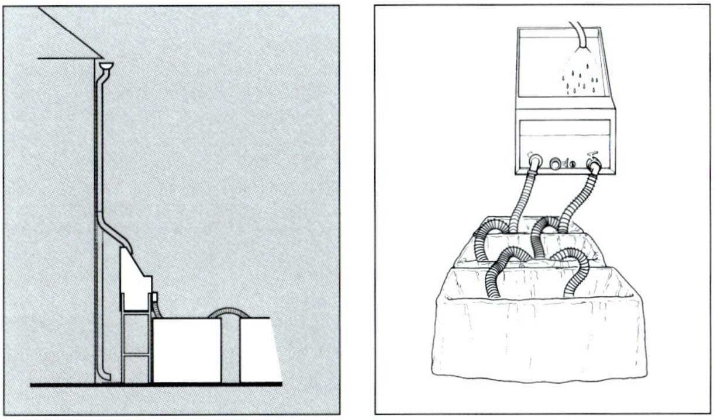

The contractor should use a collection and filter system

OTHER HAZARDS

Work at height – see www.hse.gov.uk/falls/index.htm. Take precautions to avoid falls. Must you work from a ladder? Where necessary, erect an access platform.

Work on fragile roofs – see www.hse.gov.uk/construction/index.htm. Fragile roofs cannot bear weight.

There may be other hazards – you need to consider them all.

- Put the asbestos waste container in a clear polythene sack and tape it closed.
- Disposal – see sheet em9.

Personal decontamination

- See sheet em8.

Clearance and checking off

- Visually inspect the area to make sure that it has been cleaned properly.
- Clearance air sampling is not normally required.
- Get the premises owner, dutyholder or client to check off the job.

a13 asbestos essentials

Non-licensed tasks

Repairing damaged asbestos cement (AC)

ESSENTIAL INFORMATION

Also read the following sheets in this book:

em1 (p11) *What to do if you uncover or damage materials that may contain asbestos*

em2 (p14) *Training*

em5 (p21) *Wetting asbestos materials*

em7 (p27) *Using damp rags to clean surfaces of minor asbestos contamination*

em8 (p29) *Personal decontamination*

em9 (p31) *Disposal of asbestos waste*

CAUTION

AC roofs are always fragile and cannot bear weight.

What this sheet covers

This sheet describes good practice when you need to repair damaged AC. For badly damaged AC, see sheet a14 or sheet a15.

This sheet is NOT appropriate for repairs to asbestos insulating board – see sheet a6.

Preparing the work area

- Ensure safe access.
- Restrict access – minimise the number of people present.
- Close doors. Use tape and notices to warn others.
- Ensure adequate lighting.

Equipment

- 500-gauge polythene sheeting and duct tape
- Warning tape and notices
- Mastic or sealant for gaps
- Garden-type sprayer containing wetting agent
- Bucket of water and rags
- Asbestos waste container, eg labelled polythene sack
- Clear polythene sack

Personal protective equipment (PPE)

- Provide:
  - disposable overalls fitted with a hood; and
  - boots without laces (laced boots are hard to decontaminate).
- A respirator is not normally required.

OTHER HAZARDS

Work at height – see www.hse.gov.uk/falls/index.htm. Take precautions to avoid falls. Must you work from a ladder? Where necessary, erect an access platform.

Work on fragile roofs – see www.hse.gov.uk/construction/index.htm. AC roofs are fragile and cannot bear weight.

Slips and trips – see www.hse.gov.uk/slips/ index.htm. Floors protected with polythene become very slippery when wet.

There may be other hazards – you need to consider them all.

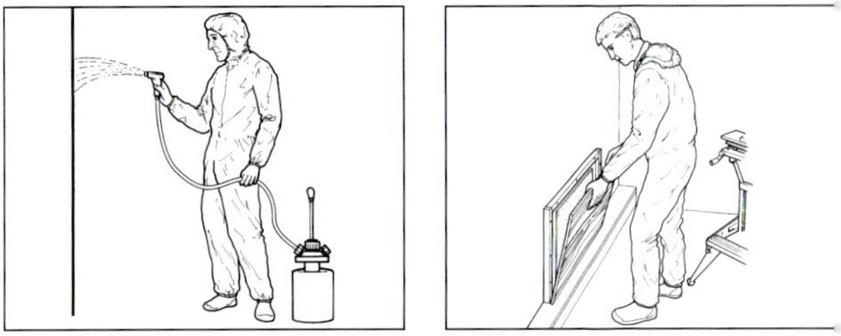

Paint or cover the damaged area, see a8 and a16

Procedure

- Protect nearby surfaces from contamination. Cover with 500-gauge polythene sheeting and fix with duct tape to non-asbestos surfaces.
- Clean up debris and loose material – see sheet a11.
- Paint the damaged area – see sheet a16
- Alternatively, protect the area by attaching and sealing a non-asbestos panel over the damage – see sheet a8.
- Warn the building owner about the presence of asbestos-containing material, so it can be managed properly.

Cleaning and disposal

- Clean the equipment and the area with damp rags.
- Put debris, used rags, polythene sheeting and other waste in the asbestos waste container and tape it closed
- Put the asbestos waste container in a clear polythene sack and tape it closed.
- Disposal – see sheet em9.

Personal decontamination

- See sheet em8.

Clearance and checking off

- Visually inspect the area to make sure that it has been cleaned properly.
- Clearance air sampling is not normally required.
- Get the premises owner, dutyholder or client to check off the job.

a14
asbestos essentials
Non-licensed tasks

Removing asbestos cement (AC) sheets, gutters, etc and dismantling a small AC structure

What this sheet covers

This sheet describes good practice when you need to remove AC sheets, gutters, drains, ridge caps, etc on a small scale, or dismantle a small structure (eg shed or garage).
This sheet does NOT apply to large scale work or mechanical demolition – a risk assessment and plan of work will need to be prepared.

This sheet is NOT appropriate if other asbestos-containing materials are present, eg lagging, limpet or insulating board. Use an HSE-licensed contractor for such work.

ESSENTIAL INFORMATION

Also read the following sheets in this book:

em1 (p11) *What to do if you uncover or damage materials that may contain asbestos*

em2 (p14) *Training*

em5 (p21) *Wetting asbestos materials*

em6 (p23) *Personal protective equipment (PPE)*

em7 (p27) *Using damp rags to clean surfaces of minor asbestos contamination*

em8 (p29) *Personal decontamination*

em9 (p31) *Disposal of asbestos waste*

CAUTION

AC roofs are always fragile and cannot bear weight.

Preparing the work area

- Ensure safe access – you may need a mobile access platform.
- Restrict access – minimise the number of people present.
- Close doors. Use tape and notices to warn others.
- Ensure adequate lighting.

Equipment

- 500- and 1000-gauge polythene sheeting and duct tape
- Warning tape and notices
- Bolt cutter
- Webbing straps and rope
- Garden-type sprayer containing wetting agent
- Bucket of water and rags
- Asbestos waste container, eg labelled polythene sack
- Clear polythene sack

AC sheets used as roofing

- Lockable skip for larger quantities of waste
- Asbestos warning stickers

Personal protective equipment (PPE) – see sheet em6

- Provide:
  - disposable overalls fitted with a hood;
  - boots without laces (laced boots are hard to decontaminate); and
  - respiratory protective equipment.

Procedure

- Check with the premises owner that only AC is present.
- Protect nearby surfaces from contamination. Cover with 500-gauge polythene sheeting and fix with duct tape to non-asbestos surfaces.

Overlaying AC sheets

- Can you overlay sheets with non-asbestos material instead of removing the AC?
- If so, attach the material to existing purlins. Avoid drilling through the AC. If you cannot avoid drilling, see sheet a9.

CAUTION

It is dangerous to seal over exhaust vents from gas-fired equipment. Can the equipment be turned off?

Removal

- Avoid or minimise breaking the AC.
- If fasteners hold the sheets in place, dampen and remove them, and place them in the waste container.
- If the sheets are bolted in place, dampen and cut the bolts while avoiding contact with the AC.
- Remove the bolts or fixings carefully and place them in the waste container.

CAUTION

Avoid crushing AC debris on the ground.

- Unbolt, or use cutters to release gutters, drain pipes, ridge caps, etc. Avoid contact with the AC.
- Lower large pieces to the ground. Don't drop them or use rubble chutes. Stack sheets carefully.
- Where there are several AC sheets and other large items, place them in a lockable skip.
- Double-wrap large pieces in 1000-gauge polythene sheeting. Seal with duct tape.
- Attach asbestos warning stickers.
- Place small pieces in the asbestos waste container.

Cleaning and disposal

- Clean the equipment and the area with damp rags.
- Check for debris in fasteners or bolt holes. Clean with damp rags.
- Put debris, used rags, polythene sheeting and other waste in the asbestos waste container and tape it closed.
- Dispose of contaminated webbing and rope as 'asbestos waste'.
- Put the asbestos waste container in a clear polythene sack and tape it closed.
- Disposal – see sheet em9.

Personal decontamination

- See sheet em8.

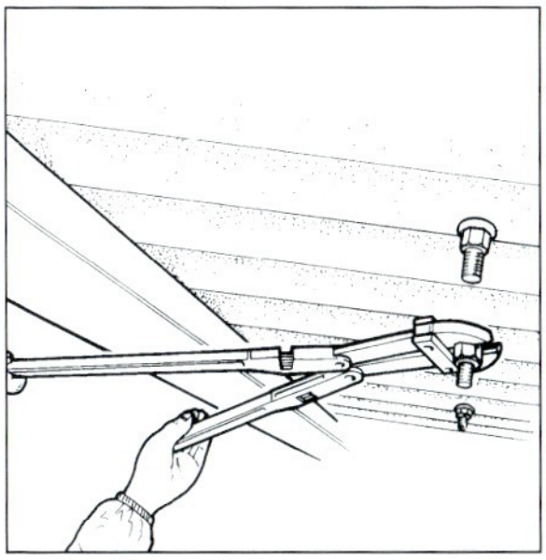

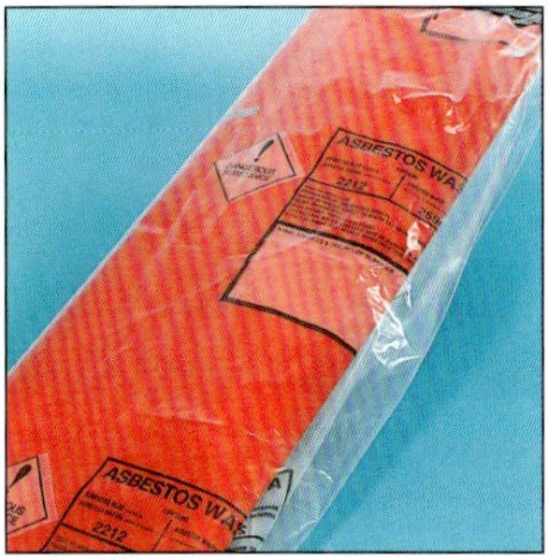

Cut the bolts while avoiding contact with the asbestos cement.

Double-wrap large pieces in 1000-gauge polythene sheeting and seal with duct tape

OTHER HAZARDS

Work at height – see www.hse.gov.uk/falls/index.htm. Take precautions to avoid falls. Must you work from a ladder? Where necessary, erect an access platform.

Work on fragile roofs – see www.hse.gov.uk/construction/index.htm. Fragile roofs cannot bear weight.

Electrical hazards – see www.hse.gov.uk/electricity/index.htm. Get a competent electrician to isolate and reconnect electricity supply.

Manual handling – see www.hse.gov.uk/msd/index.htm. Plan how to remove and handle heavy material and articles safely.

Confined spaces – www.hse.gov.uk/ confinedspace/index.htm

Slips and trips – see www.hse.gov.uk/slips/index.htm. Floors protected with polythene become very slippery when wet.

There may be other hazards – you need to consider them all.

Clearance and checking off

- Visually inspect the area to make sure that it has been cleaned properly.
- Clearance air sampling is not normally required.
- Get the premises owner, dutyholder or client to check off the job.

Further information

- *Health and safety in roof work* HSG33 (Third edition) HSE Books 2008 ISBN 978 0 7176 6250 0

a15 asbestos essentials

Non-licensed tasks

ESSENTIAL INFORMATION

Also read the following sheets in this book:

em1 (p11) *What to do if you uncover or damage materials that may contain asbestos*

em2 (p14) *Training*

em5 (p21) *Wetting asbestos materials*

em6 (p23) *Personal protective equipment (PPE)*

em7 (p27) *Using damp rags to clean surfaces of minor asbestos contamination*

em8 (p29) *Personal decontamination*

em9 (p31) *Disposal of asbestos waste*

Removing an asbestos cement (AC) or reinforced plastic product, eg tank, duct, water cistern

What this sheet covers

This sheet describes good practice when you need to remove an AC product (eg tank) or a plastic reinforced product (eg a bakelite cistern) from an area such as a loft.
If the article is no longer needed, but doesn't interfere with any other installations or work, then note its location for the building owner and leave it in place.

See sheet a35 for AC flues and ducts and sheet a23 for plastic floor tiles.

If the product is attached to asbestos insulating board, see sheet em4 on shadow vacuuming and sheet a6 for minor damage repair.

Preparing the work area

- Ensure safe access.
- Restrict access – minimise the number of people present.
- Close doors. Use tape and notices to warn others.
- Ensure adequate lighting.

Equipment

- 500- and 1000-gauge polythene sheeting and duct tape
- Warning tape and notices
- Screwdriver and spanners
- Hammer
- Garden-type sprayer containing wetting agent
- Bucket of water and rags

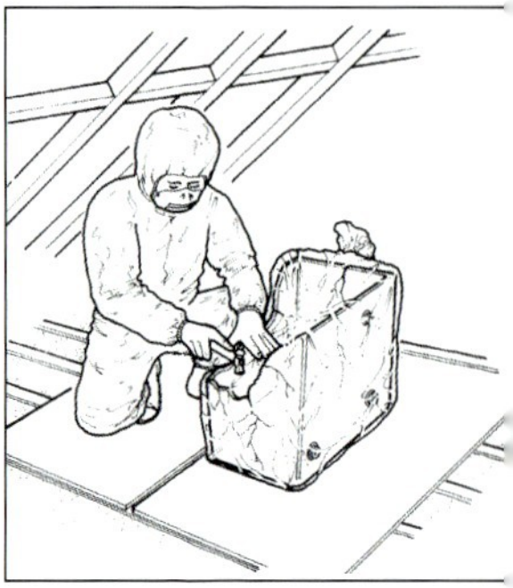

Try to remove the product intact, or wrap it in 1000-guage polythene sheet before breaking it up

- Asbestos waste container, eg labelled polythene sack
- Clear polythene sack
- Asbestos warning stickers

Personal protective equipment (PPE) – see sheet em6

- Provide:
  - disposable overalls fitted with a hood;
  - boots without laces (laced boots are hard to decontaminate); and
  - respiratory protective equipment.
- A respirator is not normally needed to remove a reinforced plastic product.

Procedure

- For lofts and similar areas, board out an area large enough to work on and to prevent asbestos contaminating loft insulation nearby.
- Protect nearby surfaces from contamination. Cover with 500-gauge polythene sheeting and fix with duct tape to non-asbestos surfaces.
- Check that the product is not fixed to asbestos insulating board.

Removal

AC product: Removal intact

- Strengthen any damaged sections with duct tape.
- Remove fittings, plumbing, etc and unscrew the product from its supports.
- Place the screws in the waste container.
- Double-wrap the product in 1000-gauge polythene sheet.
- Attach asbestos warning stickers.
- Lower to the ground carefully.

AC product: Non-intact removal

- Dampen the product and wrap it in 1000-gauge polythene sheet.
- Carefully break the wrapped product with the hammer.
- If pieces are small enough, place them whole in asbestos waste containers.
- Lower large pieces to the ground. Don't drop them or use rubble chutes. Stack sheets carefully.
- Double-wrap large pieces in 1000-gauge polythene sheeting. Seal with duct tape.
- Attach asbestos warning stickers.

Cleaning and disposal

- Clean the equipment and the area with damp rags.
- Check for debris in screw or bolt holes. Clean with damp rags.

See sheet a35 for AC flues and ducts and sheet a23 for plastic floor tiles

OTHER HAZARDS

Work at height – see www.hse.gov.uk/falls/index.htm. Take precautions to avoid falls. Must you work from a ladder? Where necessary, erect an access platform.

Manual handling – see www.hse.gov.uk/msd/index.htm. Plan how to remove and handle heavy material and articles safely.

There may be other hazards – you need to consider them all.

- Put debris, used rags, polythene sheeting and other waste in the asbestos waste container and tape it closed.
- Put the asbestos waste container in a clear polythene sack and tape it closed.
- Disposal – see sheet em9.

Personal decontamination

- See sheet em8.

Clearance and checking off

- Visually inspect the area to make sure that it has been cleaned properly.
- Clearance air sampling is not normally required.
- Get the premises owner, dutyholder or client to check off the job.

a16
asbestos essentials
Non-licensed tasks

ESSENTIAL INFORMATION

Also read the following sheets in this book:

em1 (p11) *What to do if you uncover or damage materials that may contain asbestos*

em2 (p14) *Training*

em5 (p21) *Wetting asbestos materials*

em6 (p23) *Personal protective equipment (PPE)*

em8 (p29) *Personal decontamination*

em9 (p31) *Disposal of asbestos waste*

Painting asbestos cement (AC) sheets

What this sheet covers

This sheet describes good practice when you need to paint an AC sheet that is in good condition.
Caution: If done wrongly, painting can result in the sheet failing.

To protect from impact damage, see sheet a8.

Preparing the work area

- Ensure safe access.
- Restrict access – minimise the number of people present.
- Close doors. Use tape and notices to warn others.
- Ensure adequate lighting.

Equipment

- 500-gauge polythene sheeting and duct tape
- Warning tape and notices
- Low-solvent paint
- Low-pressure sprayer, or brush or roller
- Bucket of water and rags
- Asbestos waste container, eg labelled polythene sack
- Clear polythene sack

Personal protective equipment (PPE)

- Provide:
  - disposable overalls fitted with a hood; and
  - boots without laces (laced boots are hard to decontaminate).
- A respirator is not normally required.

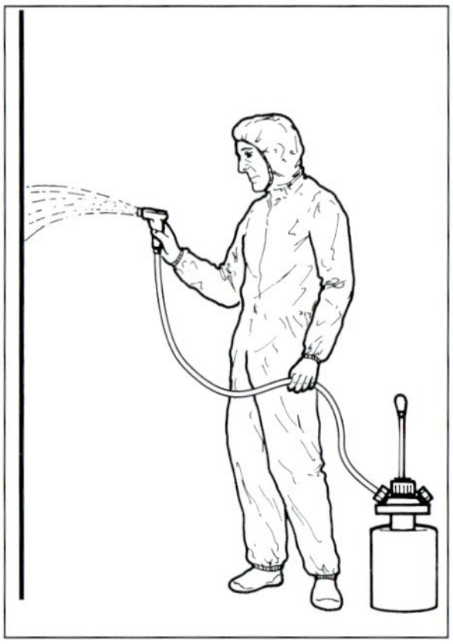

Use low pressure spraying

OTHER HAZARDS

Work at height – see www.hse.gov.uk/falls/index.htm. Take precautions to avoid falls. Must you work from a ladder? Where necessary, erect an access platform.

There may be other hazards – you need to consider them all.

CAUTION

Never prepare surfaces by sanding or rubbing down.

Procedure

- Check the asbestos cement surface before starting work. Repair damage – see sheet a13.
- Protect nearby surfaces from contamination. Cover with 500-gauge polythene sheeting and fix with duct tape to non-asbestos surfaces.
- Wipe dusty surfaces with a damp rag.
- Apply the paint, preferably by low-pressure spraying. Spray using a sweeping motion.
- If painting by brush or roller, do so gently and avoid concentrating on one area, to reduce surface damage.

Cleaning and disposal

- Clean the equipment and the area with damp rags.
- Put debris, used rags, polythene sheeting, paintbrush or roller and other waste in the asbestos waste container and tape it closed.
- Put the asbestos waste container in a clear polythene sack and tape it closed.
- Disposal – see sheet em9.

Personal decontamination

- See sheet em8.

Clearance and checking off

- Visually inspect the area to make sure that it has been cleaned properly.
- Clearance air sampling is not normally required.
- Get the premises owner, dutyholder or client to check off the job.

a17

asbestos essentials

Non-licensed tasks

Removing asbestos paper linings

ESSENTIAL INFORMATION

Also read the following sheets in this book:

em1 (p11) *What to do if you uncover or damage materials that may contain asbestos*

em2 (p14) *Training*

em5 (p21) *Wetting asbestos materials*

em6 (p23) *Personal protective equipment (PPE)*

em7 (p27) *Using damp rags to clean surfaces of minor asbestos contamination*

em8 (p29) *Personal decontamination*

em9 (p31) *Disposal of asbestos waste*

What this sheet covers

This sheet describes good practice when you need to remove asbestos paper linings (eg from a boiler casing, beneath lino, or where asbestos paper separates easily from other materials). This sheet is NOT appropriate for removing asbestos paper lagging. Use an HSE-licensed contractor for such work.

Preparing the work area

- Restrict access – minimise the number of people present.
- Close doors. Use tape and notices to warn others.
- Ensure adequate lighting.

Asbestos paper linings can be found in boiler casings, under lino or tiles and many other places

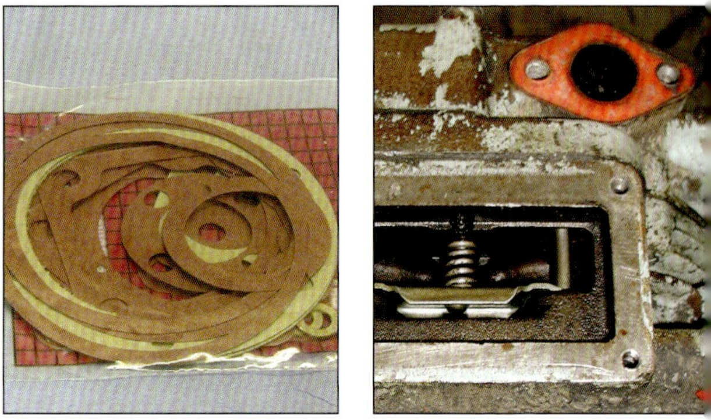

Paper gaskets can contain asbestos

Equipment

- 500-gauge polythene sheeting and duct tape
- Warning tape and notices
- Permanent sealant
- Sharp knife
- Garden-type sprayer containing wetting agent
- Paint brush
- Bucket of water and rags
- Asbestos waste container, eg labelled polythene sack
- Clear polythene sack

Personal protective equipment (PPE) – see sheet em6

- Provide:
  - disposable overalls fitted with a hood;
  - boots without laces (laced boots are hard to decontaminate); and
  - respiratory protective equipment.

Procedure

- Isolate the power supply – use a competent electrician.
- Only work on a boiler that is cold.
- Protect nearby surfaces from contamination. Cover with 500-gauge polythene sheeting and fix with duct tape to non-asbestos surfaces.

OTHER HAZARDS

Electrical hazards – see www.hse.gov.uk/electricity/index.htm. Get a competent electrician to isolate and reconnect electricity supply.

There may be other hazards - you need to consider them all.

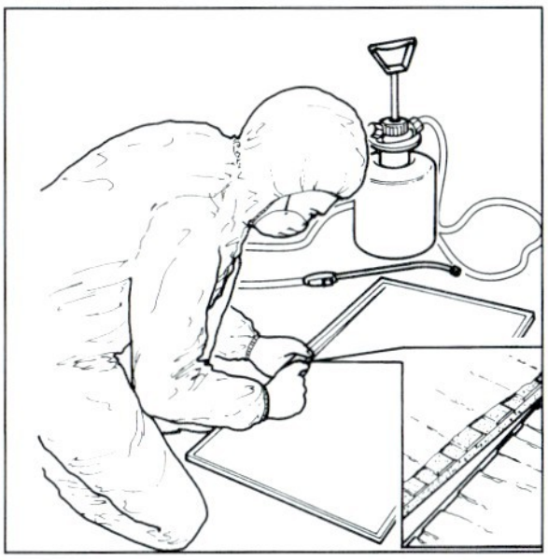

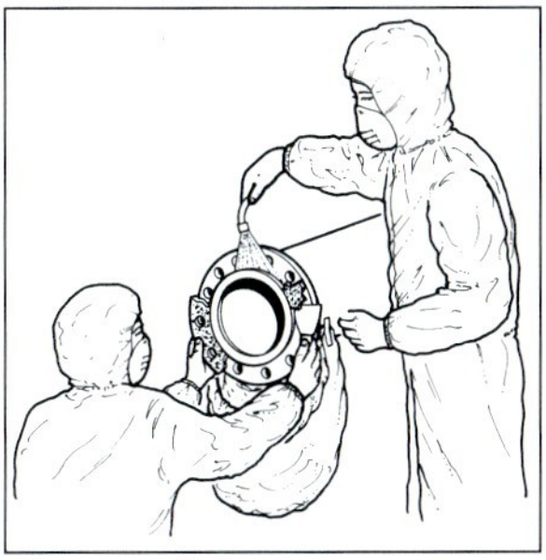

If you can't remove the paper whole, cut it – don't tear – and dampen it as you go

Removal

- Carefully remove the covering – dismantle metal covers on a boiler; ease back lino etc.
- Protect vulnerable parts with polythene sheeting, fixed with tape to a non-asbestos surface.
- Dampen the exposed paper.
- If possible, remove the paper whole. Otherwise, cut the paper – don't tear it – and dampen as you remove it.
- Put the paper in the waste container.
- Brush any paper you can't remove with sealant.
- Brush the back surface of other material, eg lino, with sealant before disposal.

Cleaning and disposal

- Clean the equipment and the area with damp rags.
- Put debris, used rags, polythene sheeting, paintbrush and other waste in the asbestos waste container and tape it closed.
- Put the asbestos waste container in a clear polythene sack and tape it closed.
- Disposal – see sheet em9.

Personal decontamination

- See sheet em8.

Clearance and checking off

- Visually inspect the area to make sure that it has been cleaned properly.
- Clearance air sampling is not normally required.
- Get the premises owner, dutyholder or client to check off the job.

a18 asbestos essentials

Non-licensed tasks

Removing asbestos friction linings

ESSENTIAL INFORMATION

Also read the following sheets in this book:

em1 (p11) *What to do if you uncover or damage materials that may contain asbestos*

em2 (p14) *Training*

em4 (p17) *Using a Class H vacuum cleaner for asbestos*

em6 (p23) *Personal protective equipment (PPE)*

em7 (p27) *Using damp rags to clean surfaces of minor asbestos contamination*

em8 (p29) *Personal decontamination*

em9 (p31) *Disposal of asbestos waste*

CAUTION

Never use a brush or compressed air for cleaning.

What this sheet covers

This sheet describes good practice when you need to remove a friction lining containing asbestos (eg brake assembly, clutch housing) or when the housing needs cleaning.

Preparing the work area

- Restrict access – minimise the number of people present.
- Use tape and notices to warn others.
- Ensure adequate lighting.

Equipment

- 500-gauge polythene sheeting and duct tape
- Warning tape and notices
- Class H vacuum cleaner (BS 8520) - see sheet em4
- Scraper
- Bucket of water and rags
- Asbestos waste container, eg labelled polythene sack
- Clear polythene sack

Personal protective equipment (PPE) – see sheet em6

- Provide:
  - disposable overalls fitted with a hood;
  - boots without laces (laced boots are hard to decontaminate); and
  - respiratory protective equipment.

Disc brake on a vehicle

Procedure

- Protect nearby surfaces from contamination. Cover with 500-gauge polythene sheeting and fix with duct tape to non-asbestos surfaces.

Removal

- Partially open the housing and vacuum the inside.
- Open the housing carefully. Use damp rags to clean inside.
- Put the worn friction lining and dirty rags in the waste container.
- Scrape off any residues using 'shadow vacuuming' – see sheet em4.
- If necessary, replace it with non-asbestos material.

Cleaning and disposal

- Clean the equipment and the area with damp rags.
- Put debris, used rags, polythene sheeting, and other waste in the asbestos waste container and tape it closed.
- Put the asbestos waste container in a clear polythene sack and tape it closed.
- Disposal – see sheet em9.

Personal decontamination

- See sheet em8.

Clearance and checking off

- Visually inspect the area to make sure that it has been cleaned properly.
- Clearance air sampling is not normally required.
- Get the premises owner, dutyholder or client to check off the job.

OTHER HAZARDS

There may be other hazards – you need to consider them all.

a19 asbestos essentials

Non-licensed tasks

Removing an asbestos fire blanket

ESSENTIAL INFORMATION

Also read the following sheets in this book:

em1 (p11) *What to do if you uncover or damage materials that may contain asbestos*

em2 (p14) *Training*

em5 (p21) *Wetting asbestos materials*

em7 (p27) *Using damp rags to clean surfaces of minor asbestos contamination*

em8 (p29) *Personal decontamination*

em9 (p31) *Disposal of asbestos waste*

CAUTION

Never unravel or shake an asbestos fire blanket.

What this sheet covers

This sheet describes good practice when you need to remove an asbestos fire blanket, or replace it with a non-asbestos blanket.

Preparing the work area

- Restrict access – minimise the number of people present.
- Ensure adequate lighting.

Equipment

- Suitable non-asbestos replacement fire blanket
- Garden-type sprayer containing wetting agent
- Bucket of water and rags
- Asbestos waste container, eg labelled polythene sack
- Clear polythene sack

Personal protective equipment (PPE)

- Provide:
  - disposable overalls fitted with a hood; and
  - boots without laces (laced boots are hard to decontaminate).
- A respirator is not normally required.

Procedure

Removal

- Where the blanket and container are no longer needed, unscrew the box from the wall and put it, with the blanket inside, into the waste container.

Open the front, dampen, and slide the blanket into the waste container

- For a blanket in a box with opening base, open the front and dampen with spray.
- Slide the blanket into the waste container.
- For a blanket in a circular cylinder: first dampen the blanket. Spray up into the container.
- Avoid over-wetting and creating a pool of water.
- Pull the blanket out, into the waste container.

Cleaning and disposal

- Clean inside any container that remains, with damp rags.
- Clean the floor beneath the container with damp rags.
- Put used rags and other waste in the asbestos waste container and tape it closed.
- Put the asbestos waste container in a clear polythene sack and tape it closed.
- Disposal – see sheet em9.

Personal decontamination

- See sheet em8.

Clearance and checking off

- Visually inspect inside the container and the floor beneath it to make sure that these have been cleaned properly.
- Clearance air sampling is not normally required.
- Get the premises owner, dutyholder or client to check off the job.

OTHER HAZARDS

There may be other hazards – you need to consider them all.

a20 asbestos essentials

Non-licensed tasks

Laying cables in areas containing undamaged asbestos materials

ESSENTIAL INFORMATION

Also read the following sheets in this book:

em1 (p11) *What to do if you uncover or damage materials that may contain asbestos*

em2 (p14) *Training*

em6 (p23) *Personal protective equipment (PPE)*

em7 (p27) *Using damp rags to clean surfaces of minor asbestos contamination*

em8 (p29) *Personal decontamination*

em9 (p31) *Disposal of asbestos waste*

What this sheet covers

This sheet describes good practice when you need to run cables through an area containing intact asbestos lagging, insulation, insulating board or coating.

If you need to remove an asbestos insulating board (AIB) ceiling tile for access, see sheet a2.

This sheet is NOT appropriate where damaged asbestos material is present, or for cabling over a suspended AIB ceiling. Use an HSE-licensed contractor for such work.

Preparing the work area

- Ensure safe access.
- Restrict access – minimise the number of people present.
- Close doors. Use tape and notices to warn others.
- Ensure adequate lighting.

Equipment

- 500-gauge polythene sheeting and duct tape
- Warning tape and notices
- Adhesive spray
- Bucket of water and rags
- Asbestos waste container, eg labelled polythene sack
- Clear polythene sack

Personal protective equipment (PPE) – see sheet em6

- Provide:
  - disposable overalls fitted with a hood;
  - boots without laces (laced boots are hard to decontaminate); and
  - respiratory protective equipment.

Procedure

- Wherever possible, use existing cable trays or conduits, or fix cables to non-asbestos surfaces.
- If there is no alternative to running cables near asbestos, protect the surfaces with 500-gauge polythene sheeting secured with adhesive spray or duct tape to non-asbestos surfaces.
- Avoid drilling through asbestos-containing materials.
- Avoid fixing cables to anything that contains asbestos.
- Ensure that cabling only runs over the protected sections

Cleaning and disposal

- Clean the equipment with damp rags.
- Put debris, used rags, polythene sheeting and other waste in the asbestos waste container and tape it closed.
- Put the asbestos waste container in a clear polythene sack and tape it closed.
- Disposal – see sheet em9.

Personal decontamination

- See sheet em8.

Clearance and checking off

- Visually inspect the area to make sure that it has been cleaned properly.
- Clearance air sampling is not normally required.
- Get the premises owner, dutyholder or client to check off the job.

OTHER HAZARDS

Work at height – see www.hse.gov.uk/falls/index.htm. Take precautions to avoid falls. Must you work from a ladder? Where necessary, erect an access platform.

There may be other hazards – you need to consider them all.

a21
asbestos essentials
Non-licensed tasks

ESSENTIAL INFORMATION

Also read the following sheets in this book:

em1 (p11) *What to do if you uncover or damage materials that may contain asbestos*

em2 (p14) *Training*

em5 (p21) *Wetting asbestos materials*

em7 (p27) *Using damp rags to clean surfaces of minor asbestos contamination*

em8 (p29) *Personal decontamination*

em9 (p31) *Disposal of asbestos waste*

Removing asbestos-containing bituminous products

What this sheet covers

This sheet describes good practice when you need to remove asbestos-containing bituminous products such as built-up roofing, gutter linings or damp-proof courses.

This sheet is NOT appropriate for work with metal cladding lined with asbestos-containing bitumen (eg 'Galbestos') - see sheet a22.

Preparing the work area

- Ensure safe access.
- Restrict access – minimise the number of people present.
- Use tape and notices to warn others.
- Ensure adequate lighting.

Equipment

- 500-gauge polythene sheeting and duct tape
- Warning tape and notices
- Sharp knife
- Scraper
- Shovel
- Garden-type sprayer containing wetting agent
- Bucket of water and rags
- Asbestos waste container, eg labelled polythene sack
- Clear polythene sack
- Lockable skip for larger quantities of waste
- For roofwork, interlocking bucket-type rubble chute into the skip

CAUTION

- It is dangerous to seal over exhaust vents from gas-fired equipment. Can the equipment be turned off?
- For roofwork, check if the roof may be fragile.
- Don't rip up asbestos bituminous felt; never burn the debris.

Built up bituminous roofing and bituminous asbestos fabric over a doorway

Personal protective equipment (PPE)

- Provide:
  - disposable overalls fitted with a hood; and
  - boots without laces (laced boots are hard to decontaminate).
- A respirator is not normally required.

Procedure

- Seal access points, eg skylights, with polythene sheeting and duct tape.

Overlaying AC sheets

- Can you avoid removal, eg by overlaying with non-asbestos bituminous felt?
- Warn the building owner about the presence of asbestos material, so it can be managed properly.

Removal

- Can you minimise the amount for removal, cutting arounc the area?
- For safe handling, cut and remove manageable sections. Place these in the chute or the skip.
- Remove adhering material by dampening and gentle scraping.
- Collect up all debris.

OTHER HAZARDS

Work at height – see www.hse.gov.uk/falls/index.htm. Take precautions to avoid falls. Must you work from a ladder? Where necessary, erect an access platform.

Work on fragile roofs – see www.hse.gov.uk/construction/index.htm. Fragile roofs cannot bear weight.

Manual handling – see www.hse.gov.uk/msd/index.htm. Plan how to remove and handle heavy material and articles safely.

There may be other hazards – you need to consider them all.

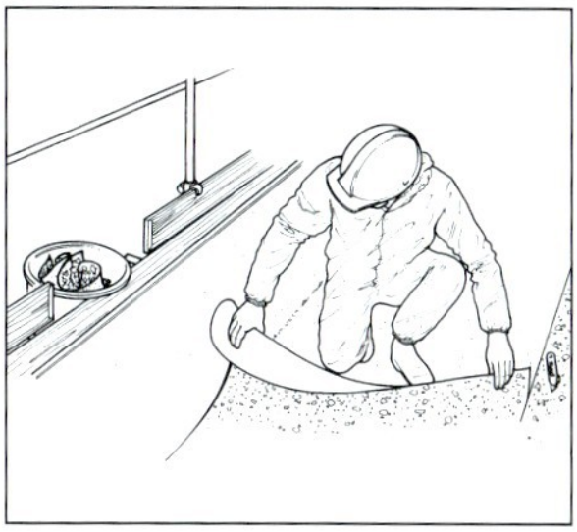

Cut and remove maneagable sections

- Remove large dust deposits by dampening and shovelling into the waste container.
- Dampen dust and debris from disintegrating felt and place in the waste container.

Cleaning and disposal

- Clean the equipment with damp rags.
- Dismantle and decontaminate the chute with damp rags.
- Put debris, used rags, polythene sheeting, and other waste in the asbestos waste container and tape it closed.
- Put the asbestos waste container in a clear polythene sack and tape it closed.
- Disposal – see sheet em9.

Personal decontamination

- See sheet em8.

Clearance and checking off

- Visually inspect the area to make sure that it has been cleaned properly.
- Clearance air sampling is not normally required.
- Get the premises owner, dutyholder or client to check off the job.

a22 asbestos essentials

Non-licensed tasks

Removing metal cladding lined with asbestos-containing bitumen

ESSENTIAL INFORMATION

Also read the following sheets in this book:

em1 (p11) *What to do if you uncover or damage materials that may contain asbestos*

em2 (p14) *Training*

em5 (p21) *Wetting asbestos materials*

em7 (p27) *Using damp rags to clean surfaces of minor asbestos contamination*

em8 (p29) *Personal decontamination*

em9 (p31) *Disposal of asbestos waste*

What this sheet covers

This sheet describes good practice when you need to remove metal cladding lined with asbestos-containing bitumen (eg 'Galbestos').

This sheet is NOT appropriate for work with asbestos-containing bitumen products (eg roofing felt, damp-proof course) - see sheet a21.

Preparing the work area

- Ensure safe access.
- Restrict access – minimise the number of people present.
- Close doors. Use tape and notices to warn others.
- Ensure adequate lighting.

Equipment

- 500- and 1000-gauge polythene sheeting and duct tape
- Warning tape and notices
- Bolt cutter
- Hammer
- Chisel
- Garden-type sprayer containing wetting agent
- Bucket of water and rags
- Asbestos waste container, eg labelled polythene sack
- Clear polythene sack
- Lockable skip for larger quantities of waste
- Asbestos warning stickers

Personal protective equipment (PPE)

- Provide:
  - disposable overalls fitted with a hood; and
  - boots without laces (laced boots are hard to decontaminate).
- A respirator is not normally required.

Procedure

- Protect nearby surfaces from contamination. Cover with 500-gauge polythene sheeting and fix with duct tape to non-asbestos surfaces.

Removal

- Carefully remove fixtures such as pipework.
- If the sheets are screwed in place, knock off the screw heads with the hammer and chisel.
- If the sheets are bolted in place, cut the bolts while avoiding contact with the asbestos-containing bitumen. Remove the bolts carefully.
- Pull the sheet away from its fastenings, dampening exposed surfaces.
- Lower sheets to the ground – do not use a rubble chute.
- Put small items and debris in the waste container.
- Double-wrap cladding pieces in 1000-gauge polythene sheeting. Attach asbestos warning stickers.
- Where there are several sheets of cladding, place them in a lockable skip.

Cleaning and disposal

- Clean the equipment and the area with damp rags.
- Check for debris in screw or bolt holes. Clean with damp rags.
- Put debris, used rags, polythene sheeting, and other waste in the asbestos waste container and tape it closed.
- Put the asbestos waste container in a clear polythene sack and tape it closed.
- Disposal – see sheet em9.

CAUTION

It is dangerous to seal over exhaust vents from gas-fired equipment. Can the equipment be turned off?

OTHER HAZARDS

Work at height – see www.hse.gov.uk/falls/ index.htm. Take precautions to avoid falls. Must you work from a ladder? Where necessary, erect an access platform.

Slips and trips – see www.hse.gov.uk/ slips/ index.htm. Floors protected with polythene become very slippery when wet.

There may be other hazards – you need to consider them all.

Personal decontamination

- See sheet em8.

Clearance and checking off

- Visually inspect the area to make sure that it has been cleaned properly.
- Clearance air sampling is not normally required.
- Get the premises owner, dutyholder or client to check off the job.

a23 asbestos essentials

Non-licensed tasks

ESSENTIAL INFORMATION

Also read the following sheets in this book:

em1 (p11) *What to do if you uncover or damage materials that may contain asbestos*

em2 (p14) *Training*

em4 (p17) *Using a Class H vacuum cleaner for asbestos*

em5 (p21) *Wetting asbestos materials*

em6 (p23) *Personal protective equipment (PPE)*

em7 (p27) *Using damp rags to clean surfaces of minor asbestos contamination*

em8 (p29) *Personal decontamination*

em9 (p31) *Disposal of asbestos waste*

Removing asbestos-containing floor tiles and mastic

What this sheet covers

This sheet describes good practice when you need to remove floor tiles that contain asbestos.
These may also have asbestos-paper backing, or be fixed with asbestos-containing mastic.

Preparing the work area

- Restrict access – minimise the number of people present.
- Close doors. Use tape and notices to warn others.
- Ensure adequate lighting.

Equipment

- Warning tape and notices
- Class H vacuum cleaner (BS 8520 – see sheet em4) for large areas
- Sharp knife
- Hammer
- Scraper
- Shovel
- Garden-type sprayer containing wetting agent
- Bucket of water and rags
- Asbestos waste container, eg labelled polythene sack
- Clear polythene sack

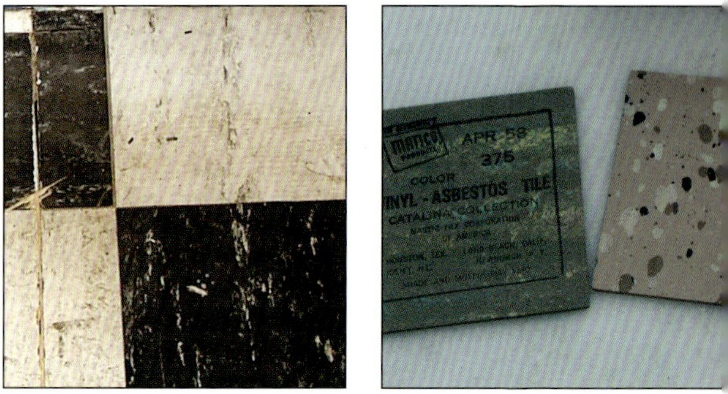

Floor tiles that contain asbestos can also have asbestos-paper backing, or be fixed with asbestos-containing mastic

Personal protective equipment (PPE) – see sheet em6

- Provide:
  - disposable overalls fitted with a hood;
  - boots without laces (laced boots are hard to decontaminate); and
  - respiratory protective equipment.

Procedure

Overlaying AC sheets

- Can you avoid removal, eg by overlaying with non-asbestos material?
- Warn the building owner about the presence of asbestos material, so it can be managed properly.

Removal

- Place the scraper in the joint between the tiles. Lift the tile gently – try to avoid breakage.
- For firmly-fixed tiles, tap the scraper with the hammer.
- For a large tiled area, lift tiles using a shovel. This speeds up the job and avoids kneeling close to the tiles.
- Spray water under the tiles as they are lifted, to suppress dust and wet any asbestos paper that may be present.
- Wet any asbestos paper tile backing as the tiles are lifted.
- Gently scrape up adhering mastic. You can soften mastic with solvent, by warming with an infra-red lamp, or embrittle it with dry ice.
- Place debris in the waste container.

CAUTION

Never sand the floor.

Asbestos-containing mastic

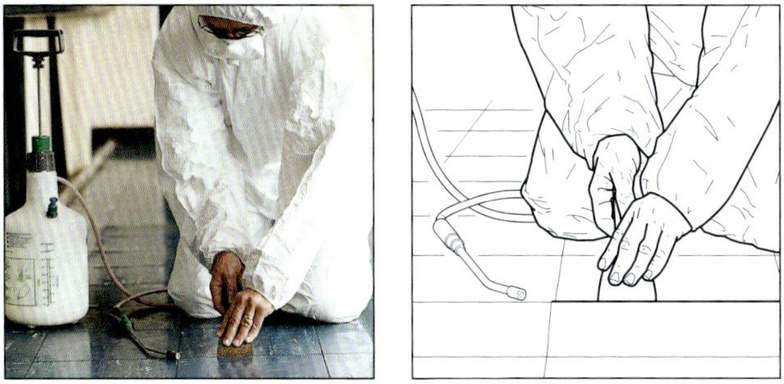

Spray water under the tiles to suppress dust as you lift them gently, avoiding breakage

Cleaning and disposal

- Where you have removed only a few tiles, use damp rags to clean the floor. Clean larger areas with the Class H vacuum cleaner.
- Clean the equipment with damp rags.
- Put debris, used rags and other waste in the asbestos waste container and tape it closed.
- Put the asbestos waste container in a clear polythene sack and tape it closed.
- Disposal – see sheet em9.

OTHER HAZARDS

There may be other hazards – you need to consider them all.

Personal decontamination

- See sheet em8.

Clearance and checking off

- Visually inspect the area to make sure that it has been cleaned properly.
- Clearance air sampling is not normally required.
- Get the premises owner, dutyholder or client to check off the job.

a24 asbestos essentials

Non-licensed tasks

Removing flexible asbestos textile duct connectors (gaiters)

ESSENTIAL INFORMATION

Also read the following sheets in this book:

em1 (p11) *What to do if you uncover or damage materials that may contain asbestos*

em2 (p14) *Training*

em5 (p21) *Wetting asbestos materials*

em6 (p23) *Personal protective equipment (PPE)*

em7 (p27) *Using damp rags to clean surfaces of minor asbestos contamination*

em8 (p29) *Personal decontamination*

em9 (p31) *Disposal of asbestos waste*

What this sheet covers

This sheet describes good practice when you need to remove a gaiter (flexible asbestos textile connector) from metal ductwork sections or from the joint with a fan.
This sheet applies where the gaiter is riveted to the metal frame, and where it is clipped in place over the ducting.

This sheet is NOT appropriate if adjacent ducting is lagged with asbestos. Use an HSE-licensed contractor for such work.

Preparing the work area

- Ensure safe access.
- Restrict access – minimise the number of people present.
- Close doors. Use tape and notices to warn others.
- Ensure adequate lighting.

Equipment

- Warning tape and notices
- Drill – manual or powered, set at the lowest speed
- Screwdriver
- Scraper
- Garden-type sprayer containing wetting agent
- Bucket of water and rags
- Asbestos waste container, eg labelled polythene sack
- Clear polythene sack

Connectors may be clipped or rivetted

Personal protective equipment (PPE) - see sheet em6

- Provide:
  - disposable overalls fitted with a hood;
  - boots without laces (laced boots are hard to decontaminate); and
  - respiratory protective equipment.

Procedure

- Turn off and lock off the system.

Method 1: Riveted flexible gaiters (duct connectors)

- Where possible, unbolt the assembly holding the connector and remove it whole.
- Otherwise, dampen the gaiter and drill out the rivets, avoiding the gaiter material.
- Ease the metal plate away. Dampen the gaiter's inner surface.
- Remove the gaiter and place it in the waste container.
- Dampen any debris adhering, and carefully scrape it into the waste container.

Method 2: Clipped flexible gaiters (duct connectors)

- Dampen the gaiter.
- Remove the clips holding the gaiter in place.
- Slide the gaiter off the ducting and put it in the waste container.
- Wipe the clips with damp rags.

OTHER HAZARDS

Work at height – see www.hse.gov.uk/falls/index.htm. Take precautions to avoid falls. Must you work from a ladder? Where necessary, erect an access platform.

Manual handling – see www.hse.gov.uk/msd/index.htm. Plan how to remove and handle heavy material and articles safely.

There may be other hazards – you need to consider them all.

Cleaning and disposal

- Clean the equipment and the area with damp rags.
- Check for debris in screw or bolt holes or on the ducting. Clean with damp rags.
- Put debris, used rags and other waste in the asbestos waste container and tape it closed.
- Put the asbestos waste container in a clear polythene sack and tape it closed.
- Disposal – see sheet em9.

Personal decontamination

- See sheet em8.

Clearance and checking off

- Visually inspect the area to make sure that it has been cleaned properly.
- Clearance air sampling is not normally required.
- Get the premises owner, dutyholder or client to check off the job.

a25
asbestos essentials

Non-licensed tasks

Removing compressed asbestos fibre (CAF) gaskets and asbestos rope seals

What this sheet covers

This sheet describes good practice when you need to remove CAF gaskets and asbestos rope seals from pipework, vessels and plant, or heaters, boilers etc.

ESSENTIAL INFORMATION

Also read the following sheets in this book:

em1 (p11) *What to do if you uncover or damage materials that may contain asbestos*

em2 (p14) *Training*

em4 (p17) *Using a Class H vacuum cleaner for asbestos*

em5 (p21) *Wetting asbestos materials*

em6 (p23) *Personal protective equipment (PPE)*

em7 (p27) *Using damp rags to clean surfaces of minor asbestos contamination*

em8 (p29) *Personal decontamination*

em9 (p31) *Disposal of asbestos waste*

Preparing the work area

- Ensure safe access.
- Restrict access – minimise the number of people present.
- Close doors. Use tape and notices to warn others.
- Ensure adequate lighting.

Equipment

- 500-gauge polythene sheeting and duct tape
- Warning tape and notices
- Class H vacuum cleaner (BS 8520 – see sheet em4) to collect adhering gasket residues
- Scraper
- Garden-type sprayer containing wetting agent
- Bucket of water and rags
- Asbestos waste container, eg labelled polythene sack
- Clear polythene sack

Personal protective equipment (PPE) – see sheet em6

- Provide:
  - disposable overalls fitted with a hood;
  - boots without laces (laced boots are hard to decontaminate); and
  - respiratory protective equipment.

Procedure

- Ensure the system has been made safe (pipework emptied, electrical supply isolated, etc).
- Protect nearby surfaces from contamination. Cover with 500-gauge polythene sheeting and fix with duct tape to non-asbestos surfaces.
- Protect vulnerable components with polythene sheeting.

Removal

- Unbolt or unscrew the flange, or dismantle the equipment.
- Once accessible, dampen the asbestos. Continue dampening as it is exposed.
- Ease the gasket or rope seal away with the scraper, and place into the waste container.
- Keep the surface damp, and ease away asbestos residues.
- Gently scrape off residues using 'shadow vacuuming' – see sheet em4.

Cleaning and disposal

- Clean the equipment and the area with the Class H vacuum cleaner and/or damp rags.
- Put used rags, polythene sheeting and other waste in the asbestos waste container and tape it closed.
- Put the asbestos waste container in a clear polythene sack and tape it closed.
- Disposal – see sheet em9.

Gasket material left on a pipe flange

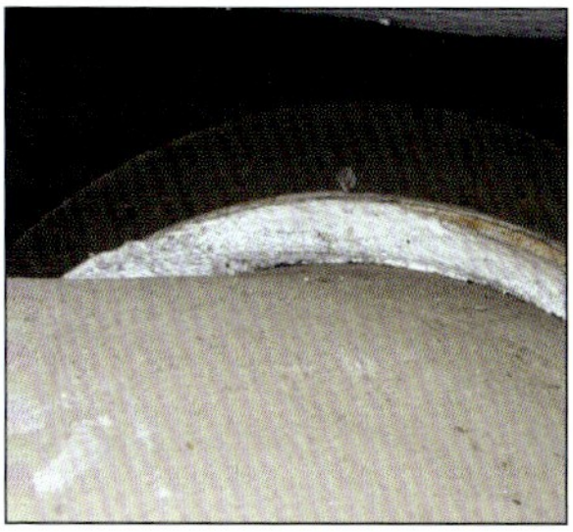

Joint packing on a flue

String gasket between metal sheets

Some examples of rope seals found on boilers

OTHER HAZARDS

Work at height – see www.hse.gov.uk/falls/ index.htm. Take precautions to avoid falls. Must you work from a ladder? Where necessary, erect an access platform.

Slips and trips – see www.hse.gov.uk/ slips/ index.htm. Floors protected with polythene become very slippery when wet.

There may be other hazards – you need to consider them all.

Personal decontamination

- See sheet em8.

Clearance and checking off

- Visually inspect the area to make sure that it has been cleaned properly.
- Clearance air sampling is not normally required.
- Get the premises owner, dutyholder or client to check off the job.

a26
asbestos essentials
Non-licensed tasks

Drilling and boring through textured coatings

ESSENTIAL INFORMATION

Also read the following sheets in this book:

em1 (p11) *What to do if you uncover or damage materials that may contain asbestos*

em2 (p14) *Training*

em4 (p17) *Using a Class H vacuum cleaner for asbestos*

em6 (p23) *Personal protective equipment (PPE)*

em7 (p27) *Using damp rags to clean surfaces of minor asbestos contamination*

em8 (p29) *Personal decontamination*

em9 (p31) *Disposal of asbestos waste*

What this sheet covers

This sheet describes good practice when you need to drill through textured coating.
If the coating is on asbestos insulating board, see sheet a1.

Preparing the work area

- Restrict access – minimise the number of people present.
- Close doors. Use tape and notices to warn others.
- A two-stage airlock is not required.
- Ensure adequate lighting.

Equipment

- 500-gauge polythene sheeting and duct tape
- Warning tape and notices
- Class H vacuum cleaner (BS 8520 – see sheet em4) for cleaning
- Drill – manual or powered, set at the lowest speed

Textured coating is common on ceilings

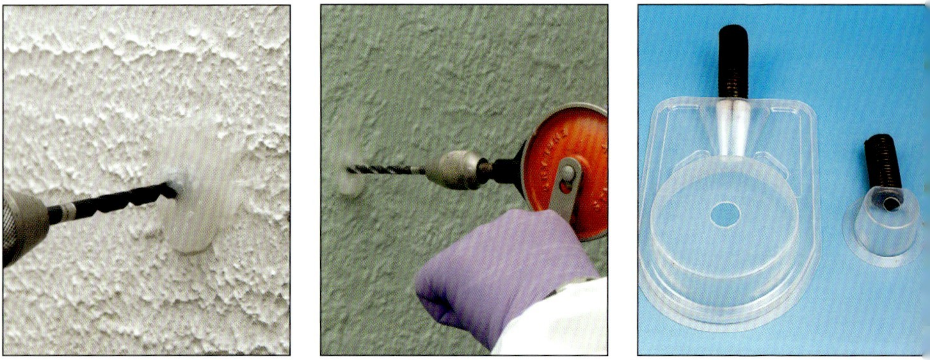

Drill through paste or foam or use a plastic cowl or other proprietary device with a Class H vacuum cleaner

- Drill bit, or hole cutter for holes greater than 20 mm diameter
- Thick paste, eg wallpaper paste or shaving foam, or a proprietary device to contain drilling debris
- Permanent sealant
- Paint brush
- Bucket of water and rags
- Asbestos waste container, eg labelled polythene sack
- Clear polythene sack

Personal protective equipment (PPE) – see sheet em6

- Provide:
  - disposable overalls fitted with a hood;
  - boots without laces (laced boots are hard to decontaminate); and
  - respiratory protective equipment.

OTHER HAZARDS

Work at height – see www.hse.gov.uk/falls/index.htm. Take precautions to avoid falls. Must you work from a ladder? Where necessary, erect an access platform.

There may be other hazards – you need to consider them all.

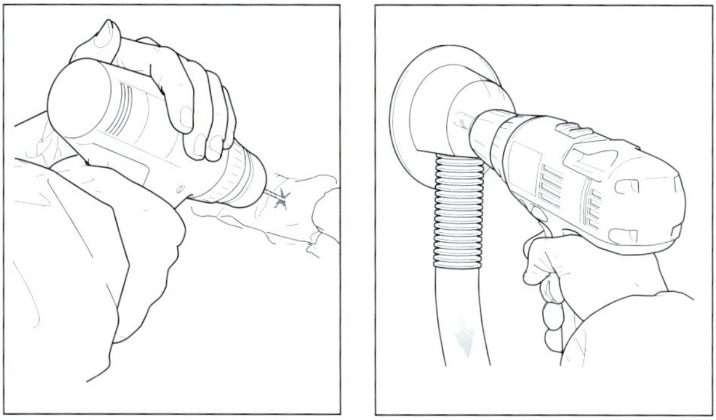

A hand drill creates less dust. If you have to use an electric drill, put it on the slowest setting

Procedure

- Remove furniture and fittings from the area, or protect them from contamination using 500-gauge polythene sheet.
- Protect nearby surfaces from contamination. Cover with 500-gauge polythene sheeting and fix with duct tape to non-asbestos surfaces.
- For cable and pipework, make the hole slightly bigger than required.

Drilling and boring

- Cover the drill entry and, if accessible, exit points with a generous amount of paste, foam or a proprietary device.
- Drill through the paste, foam or device.
- Clean off the paste, foam and debris with damp rags. Or remove the device and clean the surface. Clean the back surface with damp rags, if accessible.
- Rags and paste or foam contain dust and fibres. Dispose of as asbestos waste.
- Seal the drilled edge with sealant.

Cleaning and disposal

- Clean the area and equipment with the Class H vacuum cleaner and damp rags.
- Put debris, used rags, paint brush, polythene sheeting and other waste in the asbestos waste container and tape it closed.
- Put the asbestos waste container in a clear polythene sack and tape it closed.
- Disposal – see sheet em9.

Personal decontamination

- See sheet em8.

Clearance and checking off

- Visually inspect the area to make sure that it has been cleaned properly.
- Clearance air sampling is not normally required.
- Get the premises owner, dutyholder or client to check off the job.

a27
asbestos essentials
Non-licensed tasks

Inserting and removing screws through textured coatings

ESSENTIAL INFORMATION

Also read the following sheets in this book:

em1 (p11) *What to do if you uncover or damage materials that may contain asbestos*

em2 (p14) *Training*

em4 (p17) *Using a Class H vacuum cleaner for asbestos*

em6 (p23) *Personal protective equipment (PPE)*

em7 (p27) *Using damp rags to clean surfaces of minor asbestos contamination*

em8 (p29) *Personal decontamination*

em9 (p31) *Disposal of asbestos waste*

What this sheet covers

This sheet describes good practice when you need to insert and remove screws through textured coating.
If the coating is on asbestos insulating board, see sheet a4.

Preparing the work area

- Restrict access – minimise the number of people present.
- Close doors. Use tape and notices to warn others.
- A two-stage airlock is not required.
- Ensure adequate lighting.

Equipment

- 500-gauge polythene sheeting and duct tape
- Warning tape and notices
- Class H vacuum cleaner (BS 8520) – see sheet em4
- Permanent sealant
- Magnet
- Screwdriver
- Paint brush
- Bucket of water and rags
- Asbestos waste container, eg labelled polythene sack
- Clear polythene sack

Personal protective equipment (PPE) – see sheet em6

- Provide:
  - disposable overalls fitted with a hood;
  - boots without laces (laced boots are hard to decontaminate); and
  - respiratory protective equipment.

a26 tells you how to drill through textured coating

Paint sealant around the hole before you insert the screw. Use shadow vacuuming to control dust when removing screws

Procedure

- Can you use strong adhesive instead of screws?
- Remove furniture and fittings from the area, or protect them from contamination using 500-gauge polythene sheet.
- Protect nearby surfaces from contamination. Cover with 500-gauge polythene sheeting and fix with duct tape to non-asbestos surfaces.

Inserting screw

- Hole drilling – see sheet a26.
- Paint sealant around the hole and fix the screw.

Removing screw

- Locate steel screws with the magnet. Locate brass screws by careful paint scraping.
- Use 'shadow vacuuming' to control dust – see sheet em4.
- Unscrew – put the screws in the waste container.
- Paint sealant around the hole.

Cleaning and disposal

- Clean the area and equipment with the Class H vacuum cleaner and damp rags.
- Put debris, used rags, paint brush, polythene sheeting and other waste in the asbestos waste container and tape it closed.

OTHER HAZARDS

Work at height – see www.hse.gov.uk/falls/index.htm. Take precautions to avoid falls. Must you work from a ladder? Where necessary, erect an access platform.

There may be other hazards – you need to consider them all.

- Put the asbestos waste container in a clear polythene sack and tape it closed.
- Disposal – see sheet em9.

Personal decontamination

- See sheet em8.

Clearance and checking off

- Visually inspect the area to make sure that it has been cleaned properly.
- Clearance air sampling is not normally required.
- Get the premises owner, dutyholder or client to check off the job.

a28 asbestos essentials

Non-licensed tasks

Removing textured coating from a small area, eg 1 square metre

ESSENTIAL INFORMATION

Also read the following sheets in this book:

em1 (p11) *What to do if you uncover or damage materials that may contain asbestos*

em2 (p14) *Training*

em4 (p17) *Using a Class H vacuum cleaner for asbestos*

em6 (p23) *Personal protective equipment (PPE)*

em7 (p27) *Using damp rags to clean surfaces of minor asbestos contamination*

em8 (p29) *Personal decontamination*

em9 (p31) *Disposal of asbestos waste*

em10 (p33) *Statement of cleanliness after textured coating removal*

What this sheet covers

This sheet describes good practice when you need to remove a small area of textured coating, eg around 1 square metre, in preparation for other maintenance work.
This sheet is NOT appropriate for large areas. The work is still non-licensed but you need to make a risk assessment.

If the coating covers asbestos insulating board, use an HSE-licensed contractor.

Preparing the work area

- Do you need to isolate any services?
- Restrict access – minimise the number of people present.
- Close doors. Use tape and notices to warn others.
- A two-stage airlock is not required.
- Ensure adequate lighting.

Equipment

- 500-gauge polythene sheeting and duct tape
- Warning tape and notices
- Class H vacuum cleaner (BS 8520) – see sheet em4
- Penetrating stripping fluid or gel, or a steam generator
- Permanent sealant
- Plastic dustpan
- Scraper
- Paint brush
- Bucket of water and rags

CAUTION

Never scrape through or sand down textured coatings or stripped surfaces. Don't use power tools to cut through textured coatings.

- Asbestos waste container, eg labelled polythene sack
- Clear polythene sack

Personal protective equipment (PPE) – see sheet em6

- Provide:
  - disposable overalls fitted with a hood;
  - boots without laces (laced boots are hard to decontaminate); and
  - respiratory protective equipment.

Procedure

- Remove furniture and fittings from the area, or protect them from contamination using 500-gauge polythene sheet.
- Protect nearby surfaces from contamination. Cover with 500-gauge polythene sheeting and fix with duct tape to non-asbestos surfaces.

Removal

- Dampen and pick off any loose pieces of coating and put them in the waste container.
- Either brush on penetrating fluid gently, or dampen and loosen the coating with steam.
- When loose, gently scrape the coating into the dustpan. Empty this into the waste container.
- Seal the stripped surface with sealant.

Gently brush on penetrating fluid, or dampen and loosen the coating with steam

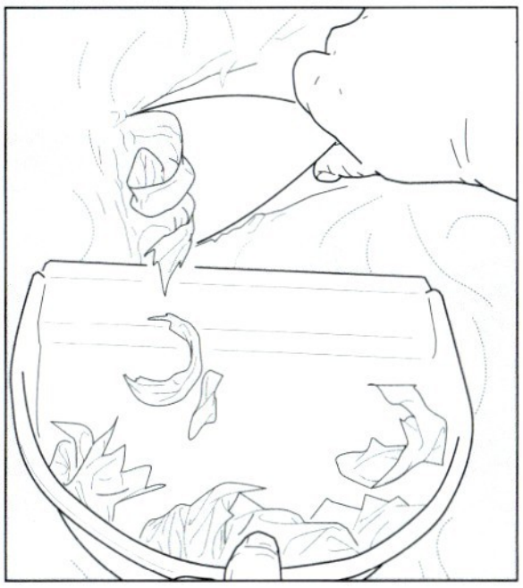

Gently scrape the coating into the dustpan

OTHER HAZARDS

Work at height – see www.hse.gov.uk/falls/index.htm. Take precautions to avoid falls. Must you work from a ladder? Where necessary, erect an access platform.

Slips and trips – see www.hse.gov.uk/slips/index.htm. Floors protected with polythene become very slippery when wet.

There may be other hazards – you need to consider them all.

Cleaning and disposal

- Clean the area and equipment with the Class H vacuum cleaner and damp rags.
- Put debris, used rags, paint brush, polythene sheeting and other waste in the asbestos waste container and tape it closed.
- Put the asbestos waste container in a clear polythene sack and tape it closed.
- Disposal - see sheet em9.

Personal decontamination

- See sheet em8.

Clearance and checking off

- Visually inspect the area to make sure that it has been cleaned properly.
- Clearance air sampling is not normally required.
- Provide a statement – see sheet em10.
- Get the premises owner, dutyholder or client to check off the job.

a29
asbestos essentials
Non-licensed tasks

Clearing up debris following collapse of a ceiling or wall covered with textured coating

ESSENTIAL INFORMATION

Also read the following sheets in this book:

em1 (p11) *What to do if you uncover or damage materials that may contain asbestos*

em2 (p14) *Training*

em4 (p17) *Using a Class H vacuum cleaner for asbestos*

em6 (p23) *Personal protective equipment (PPE)*

em7 (p27) *Using damp rags to clean surfaces of minor asbestos contamination*

em8 (p29) *Personal decontamination*

em9 (p31) *Disposal of asbestos waste*

What this sheet covers

This sheet describes good practice when you need to clear up wall or ceiling debris with a textured coating.
This sheet does NOT apply to the removal or renovation of remaining coatings.

It is NOT appropriate if the coating covers asbestos insulating board. Use an HSE-licensed contractor for such work.

Preparing the work area

- Ensure that the area is safe to enter.
- Do you need to isolate any services?
- Restrict access – minimise the number of people present.
- A two-stage airlock is not required.
- Ensure adequate lighting.

Equipment

- Warning tape and notices
- Class H vacuum cleaner (BS 8520) – see sheet em4
- Scoop or trowel
- Shovel
- Bucket of water and rags
- Asbestos waste container, eg labelled polythene sack
- Lockable skip for larger quantities of waste
- Clear polythene sack

Old lath and plaster ceilings are often covered in textured coating to hide imperfections

OTHER HAZARDS

Manual handling – see www.hse.gov.uk/msd/index.htm. Plan how to remove and handle heavy material and articles safely.

Electrical hazards – see www.hse.gov.uk/electricity/index.htm. Get a competent electrician to isolate and reconnect electricity supply.

There may be other hazards – you need to consider them all.

Personal protective equipment (PPE) - see sheet em6

- Provide:
  - disposable overalls fitted with a hood;
  - boots without laces (laced boots are hard to decontaminate); and
  - respiratory protective equipment.

Procedure

- Shovel or scoop smaller pieces into the asbestos waste container.
- Put larger amounts in the lockable skip.

Cleaning and disposal

- Clean contaminated furniture and furnishings with the Class H vacuum cleaner.
- Wrap cleaned furniture in polythene sheeting. Remove cleaned furnishings.
- Dispose of any contaminated furniture or furnishings that cannot be cleaned.
- Clean the equipment and the area with damp rags.
- Put debris, used rags and other waste in the asbestos waste container and tape it closed.
- Put the asbestos waste container in a clear polythene sack and tape it closed.
- Disposal – see sheet em9.

Personal decontamination

- See sheet em8.

Clearance and checking off

- Visually inspect the area to make sure that it has been cleaned properly.
- Clearance air sampling is not normally required.
- Get the premises owner, dutyholder or client to check off the job.

a30 asbestos essentials

Non-licensed tasks

ESSENTIAL INFORMATION

Also read the following sheets in this book:

em1 (p11) *What to do if you uncover or damage materials that may contain asbestos*

em2 (p14) *Training*

em4 (p17) *Using a Class H vacuum cleaner for asbestos*

em6 (p23) *Personal protective equipment (PPE)*

em7 (p27) *Using damp rags to clean surfaces of minor asbestos contamination*

em8 (p29) *Personal decontamination*

em9 (p31) *Disposal of asbestos waste*

Removing an asbestos-containing 'Arc shield' from electrical switchgear

What this sheet covers

This sheet describes good practice when you need to remove an arc shield.

Preparing the work area

- Have a competent electrician isolate and lock off the electricity supply, and test to show that the system is not live.
- Restrict access – minimise the number of people present.
- Close doors. Use tape and notices to warn others.
- Ensure adequate lighting.

Equipment

- 500-gauge polythene sheeting and duct tape
- Warning tape and notices
- Class H vacuum cleaner (BS 8520) – see sheet em4
- Screwdriver and spanners
- Non-asbestos replacement arc shield
- Bucket of water and rags
- Asbestos waste container, eg labelled polythene sack
- Clear polythene sack

Personal protective equipment (PPE) – see sheet em6

- Provide:
  - disposable overalls fitted with a hood;
  - boots without laces (laced boots are hard to decontaminate); and
  - respiratory protective equipment.

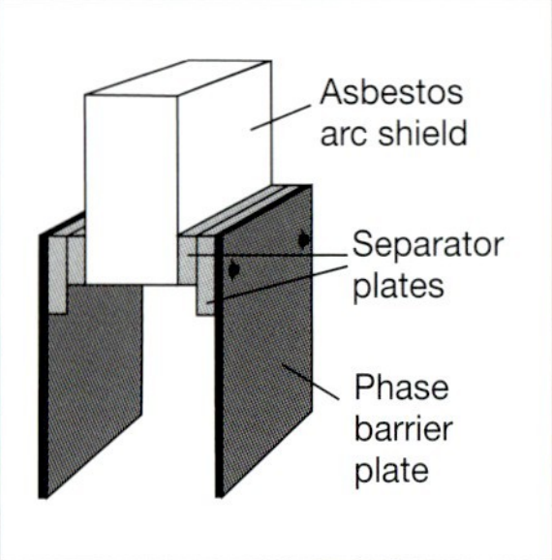

Arc shield

Procedure

- Pre-clean the area. Vacuum, then wipe surfaces with damp rags.
- Protect nearby surfaces from contamination. Cover with 500-gauge polythene sheeting and fix with duct tape to non-asbestos surfaces.

Removal

- Unbolt or unscrew using 'shadow vacuuming' – see sheet em4.
- Remove the bolts or fixings carefully and place them in the waste container.
- Loosen and remove the arc shield. Put it in the waste container.
- Gently scrape off residues using 'shadow vacuuming' – see sheet em4.
- Vacuum clean and wipe all surfaces.
- Install the new arc shield.

Cleaning and disposal

- Clean the equipment and the area with damp rags.
- Put used rags, polythene sheeting and other waste in the asbestos waste container and tape it closed.
- Put the asbestos waste container in a clear polythene sack and tape it closed.
- Disposal – see sheet em9.

Personal decontamination

- See sheet em8.

Clearance and checking off

- Visually inspect the area to make sure that it has been cleaned properly.
- Clearance air sampling is not normally required.
- Get the premises owner, dutyholder or client to check off the job.

OTHER HAZARDS

Electrical hazards – see www.hse.gov.uk/electricity/index.htm. Get a competent electrician to isolate and reconnect electricity supply.

There may be other hazards – you need to consider them all.

a31 asbestos essentials

Non-licensed tasks

Removing a single asbestos-containing gas or electric heater

ESSENTIAL INFORMATION

Also read the following sheets in this book:

em1 (p11) *What to do if you uncover or damage materials that may contain asbestos*

em2 (p14) *Training*

em4 (p17) *Using a Class H vacuum cleaner for asbestos*

em5 (p21) *Wetting asbestos materials*

em6 (p23) *Personal protective equipment (PPE)*

em7 (p27) *Using damp rags to clean surfaces of minor asbestos contamination*

em8 (p29) *Personal decontamination*

em9 (p31) *Disposal of asbestos waste*

What this sheet covers

This sheet describes good practice when you need to remove:

- **a single gas heater (catalytic, radiant, coal- or log-effect); or**
- **an electric heater (storage, radiant, etc).**

This sheet is NOT appropriate if the work involves asbestos insulating board and lasts more than one hour a week for a worker, or more than two hours in total for two or more workers. Use an HSE-licensed contractor for such work.

You must use a Gas Safe-registered engineer to disconnect and make safe gas appliances.

Preparing the work area

- Have a competent electrician to isolate the appliance from the electricity supply.
- Restrict access – minimise the number of people present.
- Close doors. Use tape and notices to warn others.
- Ensure adequate lighting.

Equipment

- 500- and 1000-gauge polythene sheeting and duct tape
- Warning tape and notices
- Class H vacuum cleaner (BS 8520) – see sheet em4
- Screwdriver and spanners
- Garden-type sprayer containing wetting agent
- Bucket of water and rags

OTHER HAZARDS

Electrical hazards – see www.hse.gov.uk/electricity/index.htm. Get a competent electrician to isolate and reconnect electricity supply.

Manual handling – see www.hse.gov.uk/msd/index.htm. Plan how to remove and handle heavy material and articles safely.

Gas safety – check your contractor's registration at www.gassaferegister.co.uk/

There may be other hazards – you need to consider them all.

- Asbestos waste container, eg labelled polythene sack
- Asbestos warning stickers
- Clear polythene sack

Personal protective equipment (PPE) – see sheet em6

- Provide:
  - disposable overalls fitted with a hood;
  - boots without laces (laced boots are hard to decontaminate); and
  - respiratory protective equipment.

Procedure

- Can you remove and dispose of the appliance intact?

Preparation

- Remove furniture and fittings from the area, or protect them from contamination using 500-gauge polythene sheet.
- Protect nearby surfaces from contamination. Cover with 500-gauge polythene sheeting and fix with duct tape to non-asbestos surfaces.
- Check if the appliance is attached to asbestos insulating board (AIB); sometimes, this is wall-mounted behind heaters.

Removal

- Remove the cover, wipe it with damp rags and set it aside.
- Vacuum inside the appliance. Remove with vacuuming all loose material or articles.
- Dampen the parts that may contain asbestos, eg panels, board, paper, string and fire cement.
- Unscrew or unbolt fixed parts using shadow vacuuming – see sheet em4. Put the fixings in the waste container.
- Remove panels or parts intact and put them in the waste container.
- Vacuum inside the carcass before removal. If it is attached to AIB, unscrew it using shadow vacuuming. Put the screws in the waste container.
- If fixed to AIB, see sheet a6 for repairing minor damage.

CAUTION

Some catalytic heaters contain loose asbestos mats.

- Double-wrap the carcass and the cover with 1000-gauge polythene sheeting. Seal with duct tape. Attach asbestos warning stickers.

Cleaning and disposal

- Clean the equipment and the area with damp rags.
- Put used rags, polythene sheeting and other waste in the asbestos waste container and tape it closed.
- Put the asbestos waste container in a clear polythene sack and tape it closed.
- Disposal – see sheet em9.

Personal decontamination

- See sheet em8.

Clearance and checking off

- Visually inspect the area to make sure that it has been cleaned properly.
- Clearance air sampling is not normally required.
- Get the premises owner, dutyholder or client to check off the job.

a32 asbestos essentials

Non-licensed tasks

Replacing an asbestos-containing part in a 'period' domestic appliance

ESSENTIAL INFORMATION

Also read the following sheets in this book:

em1 (p11) *What to do if you uncover or damage materials that may contain asbestos*

em2 (p14) *Training*

em4 (p17) *Using a Class H vacuum cleaner for asbestos*

em5 (p21) *Wetting asbestos materials*

em6 (p23) *Personal protective equipment (PPE)*

em7 (p27) *Using damp rags to clean surfaces of minor asbestos contamination*

em8 (p29) *Personal decontamination*

em9 (p31) *Disposal of asbestos waste*

What this sheet covers

This sheet describes good practice when you need to remove an asbestos-containing replaceable part in a domestic appliance. This is most likely if the appliance is a 'heritage' or 'period' piece eg cooker, washing machine, dryer, dishwasher, freezer, radiator oil stove, etc.

You must use a Gas Safe-registered engineer to disconnect and make safe gas appliances.

Preparing the work area

- Have a competent electrician to isolate the appliance from the electricity supply.
- Can you do the job outdoors?
- Restrict access – minimise the number of people present.
- Close doors. Use tape and notices to warn others.
- Ensure adequate lighting.

Equipment

- 500-gauge polythene sheeting and duct tape
- Warning tape and notices
- Class H vacuum cleaner (BS 8520) – see sheet em4
- Screwdriver and spanners
- Scraper
- Non-asbestos replacement part
- Garden-type sprayer containing wetting agent, eg diluted washing-up liquid
- Bucket of water and rags

- Asbestos waste container, eg labelled polythene sack
- Clear polythene sack

Personal protective equipment (PPE) – see sheet em6

- Provide:
  - disposable overalls fitted with a hood;
  - boots without laces (laced boots are hard to decontaminate); and
  - respiratory protective equipment.

Procedure

- Protect nearby surfaces from contamination. Cover with 500-gauge polythene sheeting and fix with duct tape to non-asbestos surfaces.
- Protect vulnerable components with polythene sheeting.

Removal

- Vacuum inside the appliance. Remove with vacuuming all loose material or articles.
- Unscrew or unbolt fixed parts using shadow vacuuming – see sheet em4. Put the fixings in the waste container.
- Once accessible, dampen the asbestos. Continue dampening as it is exposed.
- Ease the asbestos away, into the waste container.
- Gently scrape off residues using 'shadow vacuuming' – see sheet em4.
- Clean using damp rags and fit the replacement part.

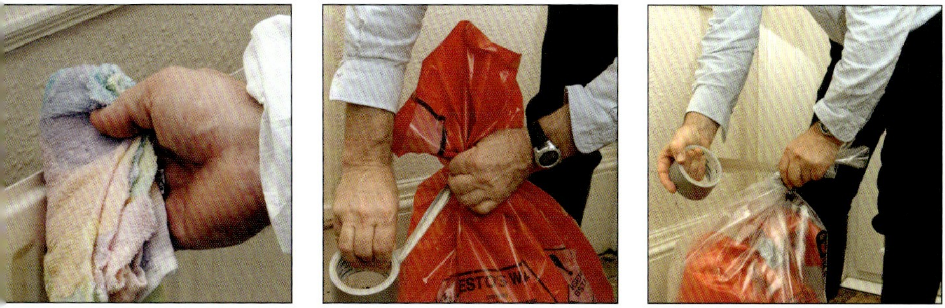

Clean up with damp rags and the Class H vacuum cleaner. Double-bag used rags, polythene sheeting and other waste

OTHER HAZARDS

Electrical hazards – see www.hse.gov.uk/electricity/index.htm. Get a competent electrician to isolate and reconnect electricity supply.

Slips and trips – see www.hse.gov.uk/slips/ index.htm. Floors protected with polythene become very slippery when wet.

Gas safety – check your contractor's registration at www.gassaferegister.co.uk/

There may be other hazards – you need to consider them all.

Cleaning and disposal

- Clean the appliance, the area and equipment with the Class H vacuum cleaner and damp rags.
- Put used rags, polythene sheeting and other waste in the asbestos waste container and tape it closed.
- Put the asbestos waste container in a clear polythene sack and tape it closed.
- Disposal – see sheet em9.

Personal decontamination

- See sheet em8.

Clearance and checking off

- Visually inspect the area to make sure that it has been cleaned properly.
- Clearance air sampling is not normally required.
- Get the premises owner, dutyholder or client to check off the job.

a33 asbestos essentials

Non-licensed tasks

Replacing an asbestos-containing fuse box or a single fuse assembly

ESSENTIAL INFORMATION

Also read the following sheets in this book:

em1 (p11) *What to do if you uncover or damage materials that may contain asbestos*

em2 (p14) *Training*

em4 (p17) *Using a Class H vacuum cleaner for asbestos*

em6 (p23) *Personal protective equipment (PPE)*

em7 (p27) *Using damp rags to clean surfaces of minor asbestos contamination*

em8 (p29) *Personal decontamination*

em9 (p31) *Disposal of asbestos waste*

What this sheet covers

This sheet describes good practice when you need to remove a single asbestos-containing fuse assembly or an asbestos-containing fuse box.

Preparing the work area

- Have a competent electrician isolate and lock off the electricity supply, and test to show that the system is not live.
- Restrict access – minimise the number of people present.
- Close doors. Use tape and notices to warn others.
- Ensure adequate lighting.

Equipment

- 500-gauge polythene sheeting and duct tape
- Warning tape and notices
- Class H vacuum cleaner (BS 8520) – see sheet em4
- Screwdriver
- Non-asbestos replacement fuse box
- Bucket of water and rags
- Asbestos waste container, eg labelled polythene sack
- Clear polythene sack

Old style fuse-boxes contain asbestos inside the fuse assemblies and must be handled correctly

Personal protective equipment (PPE) – see sheet em6

- Provide:
  - disposable overalls fitted with a hood;
  - boots without laces (laced boots are hard to decontaminate); and
  - respiratory protective equipment.

Procedure

- Instead of a single fuse assembly, can you replace the whole fuse box?
- Protect nearby surfaces from contamination. Cover with 500-gauge polythene sheeting and fix with duct tape to non-asbestos surfaces.
- Check if the fuse box is attached to asbestos insulating board (AIB).
- Vacuum clean around and inside the fuse box.

Removal: Fuse box

- Remove connections and carefully unscrew using 'shadow vacuuming' – see sheet em4.
- Place the screws in the waste container.
- Loosen and remove the fuse box. Put it in the waste container.
- Vacuum clean and wipe all surfaces.
- Install the new fuse box – attach it to a non-asbestos surface.
- If the fuse box had been attached to AIB, see sheet a6 to repair minor damage.

Removal: Fuse assembly

- Unplug the fuse carrier and put it in the asbestos waste container.
- Vacuum the fuse holder with the Class H vacuum cleaner. Unscrew the connections.
- Unscrew the fuse holder with 'shadow vacuuming' – see sheet em4.
- Put screws and the fuse holder in the waste container.
- Vacuum and wipe clean the connectors.
- Install the non-asbestos replacement assembly.

Cleaning and disposal

- Clean the area and equipment with the Class H vacuum cleaner and damp rags.
- Put used rags, polythene sheeting and other waste in the asbestos waste container and tape it closed.
- Put the asbestos waste container in a clear polythene sack and tape it closed.
- Disposal – see sheet em9.

Personal decontamination

- See sheet em8.

After cleaning, put used rags, polythene sheeting and other waste in the asbestos waste container and tape it closed

OTHER HAZARDS

Work at height – see www.hse.gov.uk/falls/index.htm. Take precautions to avoid falls. Must you work from a ladder? Where necessary, erect an access platform.

Electrical hazards – see www.hse.gov.uk/electricity/index.htm. Get a competent electrician to isolate and reconnect electricity supply.

There may be other hazards – you need to consider them all.

Clearance and checking off

- Visually inspect the area to make sure that it has been cleaned properly.
- Clearance air sampling is not normally required.
- Get the premises owner, dutyholder or client to check off the job.

a34 asbestos essentials

Non-licensed tasks

ESSENTIAL INFORMATION

Also read the following sheets in this book:

em1 (p11) *What to do if you uncover or damage materials that may contain asbestos*

em2 (p14) *Training*

em6 (p23) *Personal protective equipment (PPE)*

em7 (p27) *Using damp rags to clean surfaces of minor asbestos contamination*

em8 (p29) *Personal decontamination*

Removing pins and nails from an asbestos insulating board (AIB) panel

What this sheet covers

This sheet describes good practice when you need to remove pins or nails from an AIB panel.

Preparing the work area

- Can you do this work from ground level?
- Restrict access – minimise the number of people present.

Equipment

- Thick paste, eg wallpaper paste or shaving foam
- Permanent sealant
- Filler
- Pliers
- Paint brush
- Bucket of water and rags
- Waste bag, eg polythene sack

Personal protective equipment (PPE) – see sheet em6

- Provide:
  - disposable overalls fitted with a hood;
  - boots without laces (laced boots are hard to decontaminate); and
  - protective gloves. Select single use gloves.
- A respirator is not normally required.

OTHER HAZARDS

Work at height – see www.hse.gov.uk/falls/index.htm. Take precautions to avoid falls. Must you work from a ladder? Where necessary, erect an access platform.

There may be other hazards – you need to consider them all.

Procedure

- If the nail/pin is flush with the surface, removal will damage AIB. Either paint over it, or get an HSE-licensed contractor for removal.
- Apply a generous amount of paste/foam around the nail/pin.
- Extract the nail/pin with pliers and put it in the waste bag.
- Wipe off remaining paste/foam with a damp rag and put it in the waste bag.
- Put filler in the small hole and paint over it.

Cleaning and disposal

- Clean the area with damp rags.
- Put used rags, paint brush, gloves and other waste in the waste container and tape it closed.
- The waste is less than 0.1% asbestos. It may be disposed with general refuse.

Personal decontamination

- See sheet em8.

Clearance and checking off

- Visually inspect the area to make sure that it has been cleaned properly.
- Clearance air sampling is not normally required.
- Get the premises owner, dutyholder or client to check off the job.

a35 asbestos essentials

Non-licensed tasks

Replacing an asbestos cement (AC) flue or duct

ESSENTIAL INFORMATION

Also read the following sheets in this book:

em1 (p11) *What to do if you uncover or damage materials that may contain asbestos*

em2 (p14) *Training*

em4 (p17) *Using a Class H vacuum cleaner for asbestos*

em5 (p21) *Wetting asbestos materials*

em6 (p23) *Personal protective equipment (PPE)*

em7 (p27) *Using damp rags to clean surfaces of minor asbestos contamination*

em8 (p29) *Personal decontamination*

em9 (p31) *Disposal of asbestos waste*

What this sheet covers

This sheet describes good practice when you need to mend urgently, then replace, an asbestos cement flue or air duct. Sometimes, the joints are sealed with asbestos string.

Preparing the work area

- Ensure safe access.
- Restrict access – minimise the number of people present.
- Close doors. Use tape and notices to warn others.
- Ensure adequate lighting.

Equipment

- Mini-enclosure for nailed-on AIB – see sheet em3
- 500- and 1000-gauge polythene sheeting and duct tape
- Warning tape and notices
- Class H vacuum cleaner (BS 8520) – see sheet em4
- Screwdriver
- Hammer
- Non-asbestos replacement flue/duct and sealant
- Garden-type sprayer containing wetting agent
- Bucket of water and rags
- Asbestos waste container, eg labelled polythene sack
- Clear polythene sack
- Asbestos warning stickers

OTHER HAZARDS

Work at height – see www.hse.gov.uk/falls/index.htm. Take precautions to avoid falls. Must you work from a ladder? Where necessary, erect an access platform.

Manual handling – see www.hse.gov.uk/msd/index.htm. Plan how to remove and handle heavy material and articles safely.

Slips and trips – see www.hse.gov.uk/slips/ index.htm. Floors protected with polythene become very slippery when wet.

There may be other hazards – you need to consider them all.

Personal protective equipment (PPE) – see sheet em6

- Provide:
  - disposable overalls fitted with a hood;
  - boots without laces (laced boots are hard to decontaminate); and
  - respiratory protective equipment.

Procedure

- Dampen any AC debris with spray.
- Pick up larger pieces of debris. Put them in the waste container.
- Clean contaminated surfaces with damp rags, then put these in the waste container.
- Protect surfaces from further contamination – cover with 500-gauge polythene sheeting and fix with duct tape to non-asbestos surfaces.

Emergency repair (eg 1 to 2 days only)

- Wrap the duct or flue with duct tape – replace the part as soon as possible.

Replacement

- Turn off equipment vented by the flue or fed by the duct.
- If hot, wait for the flue to cool.
- Dampen the AC flue/duct and joint seals.
- If the section can be removed intact, strengthen the damaged sections with duct tape.

This section of AC ducting has already been labelled

Sometimes, the joints are sealed with asbestos string

CAUTION

Also remove asbestos fragments that fall down the flue/duct.

- If it cannot be removed intact, wrap the section in 1000-gauge polythene and break it into large pieces with a hammer.
- Dampen any asbestos string seal. Ease it away with the screwdriver into the waste container.
- Gently scrape off residues using 'shadow vacuuming' – see sheet em4.
- Double-wrap the damaged flue/duct with 1000-gauge polythene sheeting and seal with duct tape. Attach asbestos warning stickers.
- Install the replacement non-asbestos flue/duct.

Cleaning and disposal

- Clean the area and equipment with the Class H vacuum cleaner and damp rags.
- Put debris, used rags, polythene sheeting and other waste in the asbestos waste container and tape it closed.
- Put the asbestos waste container in a clear polythene sack and tape it closed.
- Disposal – see sheet em9.

Personal decontamination

- See sheet em8.

Clearance and checking off

- Visually inspect the area to make sure that it has been cleaned properly.
- Clearance air sampling is not normally required.
- Get the premises owner, dutyholder or client to check off the job.

a36 asbestos essentials

Non-licensed tasks

Removing an asbestos cement (AC) panel outside, beside or beneath a window

ESSENTIAL INFORMATION

Also read the following sheets in this book:

em1 (p11) *What to do if you uncover or damage materials that may contain asbestos*

em2 (p14) *Training*

em6 (p23) *Personal protective equipment (PPE)*

em7 (p27) *Using damp rags to clean surfaces of minor asbestos contamination*

em8 (p29) *Personal decontamination*

em9 (p31) *Disposal of asbestos waste*

What this sheet covers

This sheet describes good practice when you need to remove an AC panel mounted outdoors.

This sheet is NOT appropriate for an asbestos insulating board (AIB) panel or where the panel conceals asbestos insulation. Use an HSE-licensed contractor for such work.

Caution – windows:

- **Indoor panels beneath windows may be AIB – see sheet a4.**
- **Window sills may be made of AC – see sheet a15.**
- **Windows may have asbestos rope seals – see sheet a25.**
- **Outdoor panels are likely to be AC. Check for loose textured coatings.**
- **Is concealed asbestos possible? If so, ask for a survey – see 'More help'.**

Preparing the work area

- Place barriers to restrict access and minimise the number of people present.
- Ensure safe access.
- Use tape and notices to warn others.
- Ensure adequate lighting.

Equipment

- 500-gauge polythene sheeting and duct tape
- Warning tape and notices
- Sharp knife

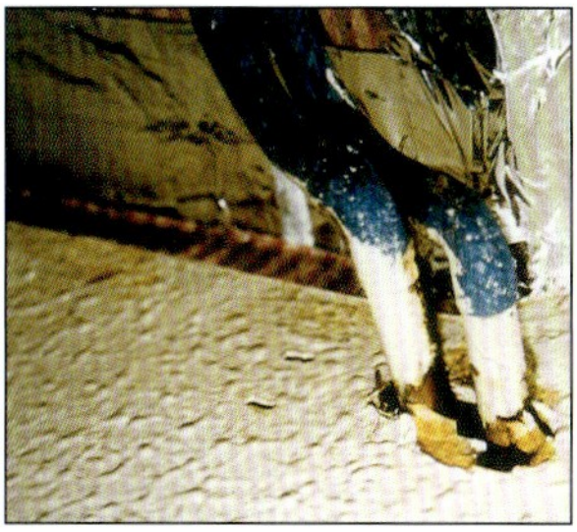

External AC panels

A lockable skip

- Hammer
- Webbing straps and rope
- Non-asbestos covering panel
- Bucket of water and rags
- Asbestos waste container, eg labelled polythene sack
- Clear polythene sack
- Lockable skip for larger quantities of waste
- Asbestos warning stickers

Personal protective equipment (PPE) – see sheet em6

- Provide:
  - disposable overalls fitted with a hood;
  - boots without laces (laced boots are hard to decontaminate); and
  - respiratory protective equipment.

Procedure

- Protect nearby surfaces from contamination. Cover with 500-gauge polythene sheeting and fix with duct tape to non-asbestos surfaces.
- Can you remove the window and panel assembly intact? Or can you remove the panels intact?
- Remove beading/nails to allow clear access to the panel. Cut beading or prise out nails. Put these in the waste container.
- If you cannot remove the panel intact, attach duct tape over the surface. Carefully break it into large pieces with the hammer.
- Lower the pieces to the ground.
- Place the sheet and debris in the lockable skip.

OTHER HAZARDS

Work at height – see www.hse.gov.uk/falls/index.htm. Take precautions to avoid falls. Must you work from a ladder? Where necessary, erect an access platform.

Manual handling – see www.hse.gov.uk/msd/index.htm. Plan how to remove and handle heavy material and articles safely.

Slips and trips – see www.hse.gov.uk/slips/ index.htm. Floors protected with polythene become very slippery when wet.

There may be other hazards – you need to consider them all.

- Place small pieces of debris in the waste container.
- Clean the exposed surfaces with damp rags to collect dust and debris.
- Fit a non-asbestos replacement panel.

Cleaning and disposal

- Clean the equipment and the area with damp rags.
- Put debris, used rags, polythene sheeting and other waste in the asbestos waste container and tape it closed.
- Put the asbestos waste container in a clear polythene sack and tape it closed.
- Place the sack in the lockable skip if you have one.
- Disposal – see sheet em9.

Personal decontamination

- See sheet em8.

Clearance and checking off

- Visually inspect the area to make sure that it has been cleaned properly.
- Clearance air sampling is not normally required.
- Get the premises owner, dutyholder or client to check off the job.

a37

asbestos essentials

Non-licensed tasks

ESSENTIAL INFORMATION

Also read the following sheets in this book:

em1 (p11) *What to do if you uncover or damage materials that may contain asbestos*

em2 (p14) *Training*

em4 (p17) *Using a Class H vacuum cleaner for asbestos*

em5 (p21) *Wetting asbestos materials*

em7 (p27) *Using damp rags to clean surfaces of minor asbestos contamination*

em8 (p29) *Personal decontamination*

em9 (p31) *Disposal of asbestos waste*

CAUTION

Don't use power tools.

Removing asbestos-containing mastic, sealant, beading, filler, putty or fixing

What this sheet covers

This sheet describes good practice when you need to remove mastics etc that contain asbestos. If you also need to remove small areas of textured coating, see sheet a28.

This sheet is NOT appropriate if the material is attached to asbestos insulating board or lagging. Use an HSE-licensed contractor.

Preparing the work area

- Ensure safe access.
- Restrict access – minimise the number of people present.
- Close doors. Use tape and notices to warn others.
- Ensure adequate lighting.

Equipment

- 500-gauge polythene sheeting and duct tape
- Warning tape and notices
- Class H vacuum cleaner (BS 8520) – see sheet em4
- Sealant, eg polyvinyl acetate (PVA)
- Scraper, trowel, hand drill, paintbrush
- Heat source (for some mastics)
- Bucket of water and rags
- Paintbrush
- Asbestos waste container, eg labelled polythene sack
- Clear polythene sack

Personal protective equipment (PPE)

- Provide:
  - disposable overalls fitted with a hood; and

Tape mastic

- boots without laces (laced boots are hard to decontaminate).

- A respirator is not normally required.

Procedure

- Protect nearby surfaces from contamination. Cover with 500-gauge polythene sheeting and fix with duct tape to non-asbestos surfaces.
- Can you remove the part rather than scraping off the asbestos-containing material?
- Gently scrape up adhering mastic. You can soften mastic with solvent, by warming with an infra-red lamp, or embrittle it with dry ice.
- Scrape off mastic into the waste container.
- Dampen plaster-based materials thoroughly with water ar scrape off using 'shadow vacuuming' – see sheet em4.
- For asbestos 'Rawlplugs', dampen and drill out using 'shadow vacuuming'.
- Paint newly exposed surfaces with sealant.

Cleaning and disposal

- Clean the area and equipment with the Class H vacuum cleaner and damp rags.
- Put debris, used rags, polythene sheeting, paintbrush anc other waste in the asbestos waste container and tape it closed.
- Put the asbestos waste container in a clear polythene sac and tape it closed.
- Disposal – see sheet em9.

Personal decontamination

- See sheet em8.

Clearance and checking off

- Visually inspect the area to make sure that it has been cleaned properly.
- Clearance air sampling is not normally required.
- Get the premises owner, dutyholder or client to check off the job.

OTHER HAZARDS

There may be other hazards – you need to consider them all.

a38

asbestos essentials

Non-licensed tasks

ESSENTIAL INFORMATION

Also read the following sheets in this book:

em1 (p11) *What to do if you uncover or damage materials that may contain asbestos*

em2 (p14) *Training*

em5 (p21) *Wetting asbestos materials*

em6 (p23) *Personal protective equipment (PPE)*

em8 (p29) *Personal decontamination*

em9 (p31) *Disposal of asbestos waste*

How to deal with fly-tipped asbestos waste

What this sheet covers

This sheet describes good practice when you recognise fly-tipped material as containing asbestos that you need to deal with.

Preparing the work area

- Restrict access – minimise the number of people present.
- Use tape and notices to warn others.

Equipment

- 1000-gauge polythene sheeting and duct tape
- Warning tape and notices
- Shovel
- Tent pegs
- Garden-type sprayer containing wetting agent, eg diluted washing-up liquid
- Bucket of water and rags
- Asbestos waste container, eg labelled polythene sack
- Asbestos warning stickers
- Clear polythene sack

Personal protective equipment (PPE) – see sheet em6

- Provide:
  - disposable overalls fitted with a hood;
  - boots without laces (laced boots are hard to decontaminate); and
  - respiratory protective equipment.

Asbestos waste discarded illegally

Procedure

- Notify the relevant authority – see 'More help'.
- Estimate the amount and type of asbestos waste.
- If the waste is spread around or mixed with non-asbestos material, get an HSE-licensed contractor to deal with it.
- Disposal – see sheet em9.

Small amount of any asbestos-containing waste

- Dampen and place pieces in an asbestos waste container.
- Shovel damp residues into the container.

Large amount of asbestos-containing waste

- Cover the waste securely with 1000-gauge polythene sheet. Peg it down with tent pegs. Attach asbestos warning stickers.
- Mark out an exclusion zone with warning tape.
- If the waste is in an inhabited area, make arrangements to secure the site until it is removed.

Cleaning and disposal

- Clean the equipment with damp rags.
- Put used rags and other waste in the asbestos waste container and tape it closed.
- Put the asbestos waste container in a clear polythene sack and tape it closed.
- Disposal – see sheet em9.

Personal decontamination

- See sheet em8.

OTHER HAZARDS

There may be other hazards – you need to consider them all.

⁄lore help

- Help to decide if work is licensed www.hse.gov. ·k/asbestos/licensing/index.htm
- For more information about asbestos, licensed ·sbestos removal contractors and training providers, ·ontact:

the Asbestos Removal Contractors Association (ARCA) www.arca.org.uk
the Asbestos Control and Abatement Division (ACAD) www.tica-acad.co.uk
the United Kingdom Asbestos Training Association (UKATA) www.ukata.org.uk
the Independent Asbestos Training Providers (IATP) www.iatp.org.uk
the Asbestos, Safety health, Environmental, e-Learning Association (ASHEeLA) www.asheela.org
the British Occupational Hygiene Society (BOHS) www.bohs.org

- Building surveyors competent in asbestos ·atters can advise on sampling to identify if ·bestos is present. Samples may only be analysed ·/ laboratories accredited by UKAS, see ·vw.ukas.org/testing/
- For lists of qualified hygienists or consultants, ·e:

the British Occupational Hygiene Society (BOHS) www.bohs.org; or
the Occupational Safety and Health Consultants Register (OSHCR) www.oshcr.org

- Your trade association may also be able to offer ·ther advice and information.
- For advice on disposing of asbestos and other ·aste, see:

www.environmentagency.gov.uk
www.sepa.org.uk/
www.defra.gov.uk/

Carriage of dangerous goods, see www.hse. gov.uk/cdg/index.htm

- Take a look at some images of common uses of asbestos on www.hse.gov.uk/asbestos/gallery.htm
- HSE's online risk assessment shows you if the task you need to carry out requires a licence, at www.hse.gov.uk/asbestos/index.htm
- The equipment and method (em) sheets and task (a) sheets in this manual can be downloaded free from www.hse.gov.uk/asbestos/essentials/index.htm
- *Asbestos: The licensed contractors' guide* HSG247 HSE Books 2006 ISBN 978 0 7176 2874 2 www.hse.gov.uk/pubns/books/HSG247.htm
- *Respiratory protective equipment at work: A practical guide* HSG53 (Third edition) HSE Books 2005 ISBN 978 0 7176 2904 6 www.hse.gov.uk/pubns/books/HSG53.htm
- *Fit testing of respiratory protective equipment facepieces* HSE Information Operational Circular OC 282/28 www.hse.gov.uk/foi/internalops/fod/oc/200-299/282_28.pdf
- *Health and safety in roof work* HSG33 (Third edition) HSE Books 2008 ISBN 978 0 7176 6250 0 www.hse.gov.uk/pubns/books/HSG33.htm
- *Asbestos: The survey guide* HSG264 (Second edition) HSE Books 2012 ISBN 978 0 7176 6502 0 www.hse.gov.uk/pubns/books/HSG264.htmFurther information

Further information

For information about health and safety, or to report inconsistencies or inaccuracies in this guidance, visit www.hse.gov.uk/. You can view HSE guidance online and order priced publications from the website. HSE priced publications are also available from bookshops.

- ✓ **Can you avoid disturbing asbestos by doing the job in some other way?**
- ✓ **Do you need a license for the work?**
- ✓ **Always follow all legal requirements.**
- ✓ **Follow the task guidance sheet.**
- ✓ **Use an asbestos waste container.**
- ✓ **Take asbestos waste to a licensed disposal site.**

Caution:

- **Don't sweep up dust or debris - use a Class H vacuum cleaner or damp rags.**
- **Don't take used overalls home.**
- **Don't re-use disposable PPE.**
- **Don't smoke.**
- **Don't eat or drink in the work area.**

If you work with asbestos:

Minimise dust:

Keep materials damp – not too wet

Use hand tools – not power tools

Clean up as you go – use a special vacuum cleaner, (class H) not a brush

Double-bag asbestos waste and label the bags properly

Wear:

Suitable disposable overalls and boots without laces, or disposable boot covers

If you take a break:

Don't smoke, eat or drink in the work area

When you finish work:

Decontaminate yourself – wipe down your overalls with a damp rag and remove them before removing your mask.

Illustration opposite shows typical locations for the most common asbestos materials

Printed and published by the Health and Safety Executive **HSG210** 07/15